THE POWER OF POETRY

Empowering Words

Edited By Debbie Killingworth

First published in Great Britain in 2023 by:

Young Writers
Remus House
Coltsfoot Drive
Peterborough
PE2 9BF
Telephone: 01733 890066
Website: www.youngwriters.co.uk

Book Design by Ashley Janson

Softback ISBN 978-1-80459-389-9

Printed and bound in the UK by BookPrintingUK
Website: www.bookprintinguk.com
YB0527FZ

FOREWORD

Since 1991, here at Young Writers we have celebrated the awesome power of creative writing, especially in young adults where it can serve as a vital method of expressing their emotions and views about the world around them. In every poem we see the effort and thought that each student published in this book has put into their work and by creating this anthology we hope to encourage them further with the ultimate goal of sparking a life-long love of writing.

Our latest competition for secondary school students, **The Power of Poetry,** challenged young writers to consider what was important to them and how to express that using the power of words. We wanted to give them a voice, the chance to express themselves freely and honestly, something which is so important for these young adults to feel confident and listened to. They could give an opinion, highlight an issue, consider a dilemma, impart advice or simply write about something they love. There were no restrictions on style or subject so you will find an anthology brimming with a variety of poetic styles and topics. We hope you find it as absorbing as we have.

We encourage young writers to express themselves and address subjects that matter to them, which sometimes means writing about sensitive or contentious topics. If you have been affected by any issues raised in this book, details on where to find help can be found at

www.youngwriters.co.uk/info/other/contact-lines

CONTENTS

THE POEMS

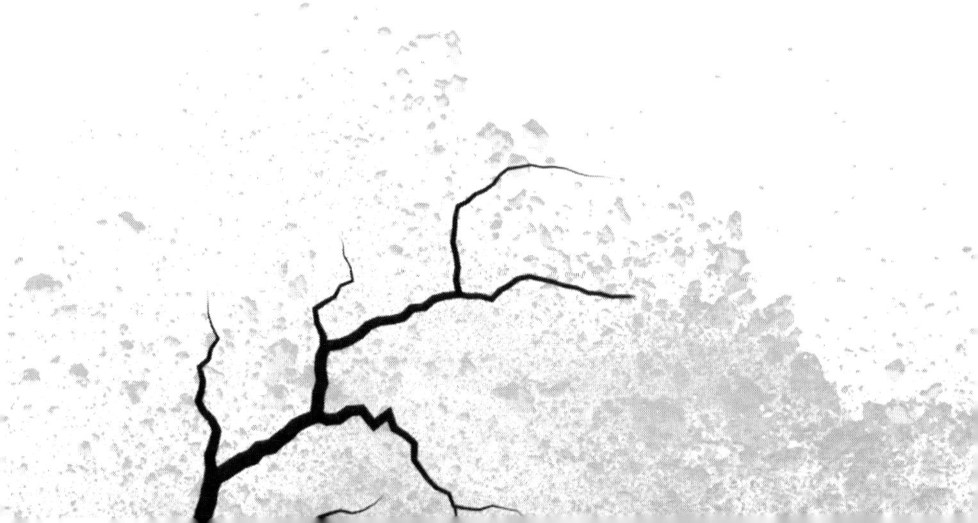

Freedom

Our people need freedom.
Young children go to fight for us but are mostly never seen again.
Who has won?
Mothers are crying almost every day about their children,
After raising them for years and years,
They go away in the blink of an eye.

This world is filled with oceans made from pain and tears.
Parents worry about their children every second they are out of sight.
What is this world?

War, every day,
People losing their loved ones every single day.
We need our freedom.
We need to raise awareness.

Isatou Hydara (11)
Holyhead School, Handsworth

Generation Z: How Distant We've Become

Technology, technology,
Is the future,
All of young 'uns stuck on a computer.

PlayStations, consoles
All the rage now.
We don't skip rope anymore.
We've forgotten how.

We are robotic humans,
Ignoring the teachings of our schools and institutions,
Oh! A new gadget, a new release
Our kind of dream...
Just flick the switch on...
There's the advertising scheme.

With our eyes wide open and being able to see,
We have tricked ourselves into this false reality.

We rely on machines for us to function,
As humans, we have become distant,
Prone to corruption.
In this technology-driven world
Oh! How we neglect time with loved ones.

The clock keeps ticking,
And the light keeps flicking,
There'll be a day where
The mourners will be digging;
Only then it'll be too late.

Wake up Generation Z,
Go out, play with mates,
Spend time with family,
Show some hospitality.

Make the most of time,
As time is precious,
Shower each other with love,
Become humble and infectious.

All I ask is we wake up,
Look at the globe,
Stop being stuck in this rut.

Love makes the world around,
Distribute it in heaps and bounds.
We are Gen-Z,
We can make a change,
By boycotting technology.

It'll be strange, but at least
We'll be human, even for a day,
I wouldn't run away,

For one small difference may make a change,
We are humans; incredible and free-range.

No, not chickens!
Read that again!
Humans!
We are Gen Z,
Care for one another,
If not for anyone,
But for the sake of humanity,
Abandon these consoles and live with a little sanity.

Asad Ali (11)
Holyhead School, Handsworth

Christmas Is Coming

Christmas is nearly here,
I'm ready to make sweets,
But everyone disappears with their spirit after a
Halloween treat.
I'm sad about the weather and a few more too,
Christmas has its ups and downs just like people do.
But Christmas is special
Kind of cold but we have Santa Claus, which is kind of old
He gives us presents or so people say,
I would not be surprised if they got scared away.
Once the holiday is over most of us are worn out
While the others are jumping around waiting for Easter
to come around.

Brooklyn Swan (11)
Holyhead School, Handsworth

Why Me?

Whoever thought the person you love the most will hurt you more.
She said they were over but I knew they weren't.
I saw the way they looked at each other whenever they talked
Why do I feel weird?
Why does it feel wrong?
Why did we stop talking
And why does she never answer
When I talk about him?
Why does it feel... wrong?
It feels like two cars crashing,
Just like a heart crushing,
Breaking, bursting, blemished.
The thing about people is they will act like they love you
Until they don't.

Anna Edegbe (11)
Holyhead School, Handsworth

Football

Football is the best,
Most people that play it enjoy the sport,
There are so many teams across the world.
It's hard to choose a team to support.

People have their opinions about football.
Most people don't like it,
There are lots of people that play football
But the people who play it the most love it.

Most people are fans,
They support different teams,
People watch it on TV,
But most get information from memes.

Mohammed Hussain Ishaq (11)
Holyhead School, Handsworth

Autumn

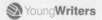

Autumn is here
It is time to fear
Red, orange, gold and brown
All I see when I go to town.

Days are shorter
Nights are longer
Around the corner
It feels colder.

Animals are hibernating
Humans are isolating
Crunchy leaves and spiky conkers
All the children are getting bonkers.

Aysha Javed (11)
Holyhead School, Handsworth

Dislikes And Likes

They're looking at me
I don't like it.
High buildings
I don't like them.
Friendship problems
I don't like them.
Being alone
I like it.
Loud arguments
I don't like it.
Loss of family
I don't like it.
Consequence
I don't like it.

Ameena Esha (11)
Holyhead School, Handsworth

Cat Poem

A rebel with claws.
I'll steal your socks,
I'll tear up your paperwork,
Break your favourite vase,
Scratch the curtains
And your hands if you stop me...
Then blame it on the dog!

Nesha Wahid (11)
Holyhead School, Handsworth

Climate Change

People are dying
Birds are flying
Water is rising
Floods are coming
Humans are running
Ice is melting
People are smelting
Animals are in danger
There is no changer.

Melan Taha (11)
Holyhead School, Handsworth

Our Home

H eatwaves flowing over our lands
O zone layer depleting
M any at risk, losing their homes
E arth is dying. Wake up!

Maliha Begum (11)
Holyhead School, Handsworth

Mother Nature

Oh Mother, we admire the beauty you have,
Our blue Earth.
From the trees, plants, flowers you gave us,
So wonderful it's a forest.

I'm so sorry Mother Nature, humans fill their desires
By making cold hard cash from your beauty.
We're trying so hard to rescue you
But everyone says 'no'.

Mother, please! We're so sorry
Please wake up!
Everyone's dying
With no oxygen.

Dear Mother Nature, the wrongdoers have been long forgotten
Now all that lies here is your reclamation.
You finally did it, Mother,
You will always have a special place in my heart.

Miriam Gombarova (12)
Holyrood Secondary School, Crosshill

To Outlive The World

To outlive the Earth would be oh so exciting,
To watch the world crumble apart,
Would not be for the faint of heart.
To think that it might not be so far away,
Makes everyone fear, for the next day.
But it doesn't have to be this way,
If we could all make a little change.
Just a little change is all we need,
To stop the trees from dying,
The flowers from wilting.
So, just maybe, now you'll see,
That saving the planet,
Could be so easy.
To outlive the world,
Wouldn't be so exciting,
If it means everything keeps on dying.

Hannah Maguire (13)
Holyrood Secondary School, Crosshill

Earth's Problems

Burning trees over seas
Homes destroyed; I'm getting annoyed
Petrol prices going up
Time to stop blowing up

Animals dying of polluted air
I think it's time we start to care
Water not being able to breathe
Because of all the plastic in the sea

How many times do I have to say this?
Time is running out
Why are we just sitting about?
When we could be helping out

Too many innocent animals dying
I think it's time we started trying
Cost of living going up
Why is this happening to us?

Freya Docherty (13)
Holyrood Secondary School, Crosshill

Friday The 13th

It was Friday the 13th of October
And let's just say I wasn't very sober
Went out for a couple of drinks with a friend
Not knowing I would walk so very near my life's end

It all started with us wanting to do something fun
The hour when the moon replaced the sun
We wanted to show those conspiracies that they were fake
Or maybe just to be out before the sun's wake

I snuck out of my room through the window
Even though to get out I had to do the limbo
As I got into Jamie's car
Ready to hit up the bar

I wish I knew what was in store for me
But I still drank that martini
While we got tipsy and danced the night away
There was a still figure lurking in the bay

We were already making bad choices
Look at how bad drunk driving is
As we went to Jamie's car
We were approached by a man with a big scar

He tied our hands and feet together
He shoved us into a corner in the rainy weather
More men in the same clothes showed up
They didn't have weapons which was just by luck

We were shoved into a big black van
While the truck moved and we were going off land
We heard the roars of the sea
Then a man came and opened the door with a key

We kicked and screamed and shouted
Then I stopped as we were threatened to be assaulted
They demanded our parents' numbers
Which made us begin to wonder

They called them and demanded a ransom
I heard my parents have a tantrum
The men let them hear our voice
But we didn't even have a choice

They locked us in this room with steel bars
And said we can just starve
We were not even thinking straight
But we decided to try and escape

We used our hairpins to open the lock
And climbed slowly onto the dock
The boat began to sail
When I heard Jamie wail

She wasn't on the dock
And we heard incoming gunshots
I ran and grabbed her
As a gunshot hit her

As soon as we arrived back
I screamed for help, for a phone that I lacked
A kind man called the ambulance
I asked to come with them and luckily they were lenient

As we arrived, I called both our parents
Told them I was okay but Jamie was with the critical carers
They arrived soon after
There were tears, the opposite of laughter

Hours passed and it looked like it wasn't getting any better
Until the doctor said she would now begin to become healthier
That news was amazing to hear
It even made me shed a tear

Don't think I got out of it without punishment
But overall, we all agree the kidnappers were demons
Us escaping alive was such a relief
Never underestimate the power of Friday the 13th.

Tamoy Cameron (12)
King Edward VI Handsworth School For Girls, Handsworth

An Adventure Around The World

As I look at the sea's great azure coat,
I begin my journey by going on a boat,
The water glistens like a sparkling sapphire,
And the engine roars like a great spreading fire.

Ahead, looms the Eiffel Tower of France,
So take a good look, you'll only get one chance,
On we go to historical Athens,
With lots of ancient museums, as it so happens.

Further travel takes me to the coasts of Dubai,
With the scintillating sun in the midst of July,
Up ahead, the Taj Mahal, what a sight!
The reflection in the water shines like a light.

Across the Bay of Bengal over to Vietnam,
The spectacular landscapes, oh so calm!
Over to the wondrous country of Japan,
Where the flourish of cherry blossoms began.

Across the Pacific to the United States,
Where an astounding experience awaits,
The final travel being over the cobalt carpet of the Atlantic
Eventually reaching English soil after a voyage so frantic.

Shriya Sastry (12)
King Edward VI Handsworth School For Girls, Handsworth

Death To Earth

Listen to the natural world around you
The chirping of the crickets
The tribal dance of the trees
As they sway to the wind's slow song

Imagine a place with no city lights
No planes disrupting the peace
Just the sweet, crisp smell of grass as it's growing
Sounds nice, right?

Do you really need the noisy cars
That makes the air stink like filth?
Do you truly desire the countless flights
From America to Greece?

Are you going to carry on living happily
In your ultra-modern apartment
With your hot showers stuffed with plastic microbeads
Your full-diesel car with that big loud engine
Your single-use wet wipes to clean your ignorant self
Your hundred thousand clothes made with non-renewable energy?

One day this world will be burnt to ashes
The sun blocked by the smog
The Amazon rainforest, a burial site for once-mighty trees
All of Australia's beautiful forests
A wasteland of charcoal twigs.

All other life long since extinct
The grass, a sepia brown
The wind that once sang beautiful music
And smelt of fresh meadows and dandelions
Now carries the scent of rot and smoke

Do you think the Earth deserves this?
This torture
This killing, polluting, this blatant-faced murder
Of the planet that has never done anything but love us?
The Earth is dying, and soon we will die too
Planet B is a fantasy
Earth is all we've got.

Harriet Binns (11)
King Edward VI Handsworth School For Girls, Handsworth

Feminist

Who I am?
I sometimes wonder,
Who is this person staring right back at me?
I sit at my mirror picking out my flaws
Then I remember
Their words that cut like knives
Dragging down from my thighs, down to my legs
Drowning in my own blood
I'm too fat
I'm too tall
With hair too short
For any man to like
With even more hair, head down
Then I remember
I don't need to be good enough
Because
I am worth more than a thousand jewels
Shining brighter than a blanket of stars
And with an entire crown sitting on my head
A crown so heavy
Only I have the strength to wear it
I am a proud feminist
I've been female for a long time now
It would be stupid not to be on my own side
So before any man tries to tell me I am any less

I remember
Remember I am not here for him
I am here for me
That this world begins with me
And ends when I say so
Whatever he says, I don't want to know.

Aila Iqbal (13)
King Edward VI Handsworth School For Girls, Handsworth

Your Protector

I will use my bones to build
You wings, so you can fly

Where I had to stumble,
You will have crutches, stopping you
Hand-crafted with my tears
And galvanised with my blood

I shall make ropes for you
The outside, from my paper skin
The inside, from the fragments of my mind
Your ropes shall be strengthened, adorned
With the shards and sweat of my soul

I have stepped on the nails left
On the roads of life
Leaving my feet scarred
Like the holes in the moon
So, when you walk
And when you fall
Only daisies and dandelions remain

I promise you my voice will be your shield
My hands will be your swords
Your demons will be safe with me
I will shackle them so you can breathe

And
When it
All becomes
Too
Much

My back will carry all your burdens
And I will fly you to your finish line.

Juwariyah Ahmed (16)
King Edward VI Handsworth School For Girls, Handsworth

Unachievable Reality

Trapped I feel, sometimes
Sacrificing what I love
For what I love
Smiles, laughter, happiness
Hope that I cannot share

Everywhere I look
But nowhere too
Everything reminds me of
Issues, troubles hardships

Caring for the flowers
Reviving all the plants
But don't anger the rain for
It can drown them too

Striving for the stars
Fighting through the pain
No pain, no gain
That's what they all say

My hunger growling
But is it really from within?
Hope you never have to feel
What it feels to
Never have control

Trapped I feel, sometimes
Sacrificing what I love
For what I don't want
Wishing the clocks could be reversed but
What's done is done.

Neha Skaria
King Edward VI Handsworth School For Girls, Handsworth

Worldwide Plea

They campaign for people to be more green
But they make no effort themselves
They urge for people to be more appreciative
But they appreciate nothing themselves
They tell us to erase the damage, to retrace
But why should they gain fame online
When we actually try to make our world a better place?
Who really makes the difference, who takes the time?
Who really wants to be more green?
Why do they just stand by and watch?
As our world turns to fumes and flames and we know they've seen
But they hold up a sign, shout through a microphone and just stand by and watch.

Tanya Balu (11)
King Edward VI Handsworth School For Girls, Handsworth

An Animal's Point Of View

My lungs screaming for air
Tick-tock
Pollution being dumped everywhere
Tick-tock
Shards of glass flying like the old birds in the grey sky
Tick-tock
Why do they dump their rubbish here, why?
Tick-tock
I am not old, I'm young
Tick-tock
Maybe we could go back to when the birds sung
Tick-tock
Probably will live longer
Tick-tock
But no, I'm wrong
Tick-tock
I can no longer breathe
My lungs filled with poisonous gas.

Keya Sidhu (12)
King Edward VI Handsworth School For Girls, Handsworth

She

She said she was fine,
but she never was.
She would smile and laugh,
but she would die inside.
She didn't want to be loved,
but she wanted to be understood.
She never looked nice,
but she looked like art.
She gave them her soul,
but they tore it apart.
She thought she was a mess,
but really, she was just a deeply feeling person in a very messy world.

Zunaira Anayat Khan (12)
King Edward VI Handsworth School For Girls, Handsworth

Falling

The ground dishing out its final betrayal
my hand grasping out one last time,
dissolving into the alluring night sky,
ridding myself of human dirt and grime.

All would be united through this process
as it takes away all feeling, pain and glory.
The warmth of the cold embraces me,
ego timeo novissimo tempore.

Aaliyah Babalola (12)
King Edward VI Handsworth School For Girls, Handsworth

Save Planet Earth

A haiku

Plastic in the sea,
Stop before it is too late,
There is no plan B.

Zaara Raza (11)
King Edward VI Handsworth School For Girls, Handsworth

Here Comes The Sun

Here comes the sun,
Shining down all around,
Laughter and cheer everywhere,
Raw light dancing between everybody's feet,
The warm embrace of smiling children,
Welcome to paradise; except not really

Sat at the window he feels it most,
Feeling the power and strength,
It gives him confidence but it's just an illusion,
Everyone respects and looks up to him

The light offers a break from the darkness he feels,
He wants to shout for help,
But his own fake laughter and cheer drown it out,
His face beaming with delight,
Despite the cogs whirring behind closed doors,
The bell rings and he is on the edge - of his seat

The sun taking the energy out of him,
Each step harder than the last,
A job well done,
The next day the sun shone again,
Not on his seat...
Instead on a wooden box buried six-feet deep.

Reece Karpal-Kelly (17)
Sale Grammar School, Sale

Freefall

They stare at me with judging eyes
The ground is shaky
My legs are unstable
The world is spinning
And everyone is laughing

The blur fades
The fog clears
But the music stops
The pages stop flicking
The TV brings nothing but silence
And I am gasping for air once more

Cold wind wakes me
A rope has me bound by my wrists
The reality is icy
Yet my universe goes up in flames
Stares. Whispers. Murmurs
Unable to focus, unable to breathe
Can you see it all
Crumbling?

The silence is too loud
It shouts in my face
It taunts and it teases
The noise is too great
It fills my thoughts

I cover my ears and wait for the climax
But it does not come
The noise is terrifying
The silence is venomous

I close my eyes
Tumbling, spiralling, into an abyss
A soft landing
But there is blood on my hands
And thorns in my heart
And I am suffocated by the vines

My best is not good enough
My hardest will never be hard enough
Far ahead of me
Far, far ahead of me
Turn away once and turn away again
I chase after the image of you
Out of breath, exhausted, worn out
But you are swallowed by the light
And I, am tired of running

A punch to the gut
Scars on my face
You spit venom from smiling lips
A kick to the stomach
While bruises take their place
I cough up rose petals
Tinted with blood

Try more
Smile more
Stand straighter
Work harder
Be like the rest of them
Fit in with the crowd
And do as you're told

The voices in my head mutter
They laugh, they scream, they giggle
They weave their ideas into my head
They make it difficult to think
They take this world, so full of colour
They take this world so full of light and life
Turn out the lights and take my colours

I plead for help, I scream into silence
The world has frozen, they watch and stay quiet
Go on, give up, there's no winning this fight
I drown in an ocean
With no land in sight

Perhaps I should've been more careful
But the feeling of falling
Remains constant.

Kalyani Kaimal (14)
Sale Grammar School, Sale

Wink Murder

I'm sure you all know the game
One person has to leave
Trying to identify the killer is the aim
But to me, all is not what it seems

They call them the 'detective'
And everyone puts their hand up to be 'it'
But from my perspective
I would never want to be the only person who doesn't know 'the secret'

Wink Murder is a lot like real life
Everyone else, but you, seems to know
And sometimes I can't help but be surprised
Why other people would voluntarily choose to

Because, let's be honest, most of the time
You are not the one to decide.

Leona Gwalani (11)
Sale Grammar School, Sale

Insensitive

Snatching opportunity, scratching
The dummies in her way,
Merciless.
Without hesitation, she will
Force you beneath the glassy surface,
She will stride above the platform
Of your open palms, as you are desperately
Cusping at the droplets trailing off her fine hairs,
As they gently infiltrate through the cracks in the floor.

Running,
Incessantly down her skin, a wealth
Just a shadow drawn by an inkbrush,
For the billions beneath the top floor,
Where the sewage from the
Showers accumulates.

Twice a week, I will fill
My plastic bucket, slowly
Dipping in a jug and raising
It above my head.
Then I dry my hair with my
Body towel, but she,
She does not listen to me!
Her ears are clogged with all that
Shampoo, her senses are

Drugged by all that perfume
Her eyes are locked-in all
That black glue.

Insensitive?
Her lifestyle has made her deaf to different ideas,
Other perspectives.
And when I finally force her out from behind
Those white curtains, she will
Slip on puddles of alcohol,
Be seen dressing herself
In resistance banners,
Dreadlocks dyed with opium.

Lips scented with heady vape, she is a woman
Burnt-out and drunk on pitiful dreams...
A woman who would have gotten us nowhere.

For years, I played a friend, soothing
Her tears with vermillion blossoms,
Teaching her how to
Meditate when she fumed.
All the while, I was drying an
Intricate fullerene of rice paper,
The wet fountain-inks of
My ambition.

A focus: calculated and determined, directing
Generations of worn buckets that sparkle, brimming with
Initiative and investment.

Yet, the extensions of time are a sensitive medium, thus we must
Draw whilst societal origami is still undergoing its next fold,
Write whilst the previous work's inks are not yet quite dry, and
Lead, because you know. What. You. Want.

You must push for those positions of power,
Because if we do not carry the buckets, then

Who will?

Alina Patwary
Sale Grammar School, Sale

War

Down they go, deep into battle.
One drops dead, then two, then three.
Gunshots so loud they make the ground rattle.
Many men lost their lives and they've all lost their glee.

So many innocents caught in the conflict.
Everyone is trying hard to flee.
Mother and child are both panicked.
Many tried to travel over sea.

Back to the battlefield where the soldiers stand.
Some barely managing to survive.
Very few arrive safely back in their homeland.
Not so many lived over twenty-five.

War is not necessary, we need to stop this.
It doesn't bring anyone very much bliss.

Srishti Mukherjee (12)
Sale Grammar School, Sale

Highway Woman

At 13:
Something's changing, something's changing
She gets this urge from day to day
Finds herself longing out the window
To run far, far, far away
Sometimes she doesn't know
If she can speak, if not to scream
Because she's interrupted and ignored
As if she's in a dream

At 14:
When the world feels like it's choking her
She imagines riding down some road
Singing proud and wild to music, and that
Lightening her load
So through thunder and through lightning
Inside she gallops to the beat
Her sisters and her mothers
Dancing with her down the street

At 15:
She says she'd love to own a steed
Ride away on sunlit plains
With her hands around no man's waist
But grasping firmly at the reigns.
She'd break the chains that bound her

No matter what they say
Rouse a gang of female pirates
Running rampant on the highway

At 16:
At this age, she thinks the only truth
Is the direction of progression
A truth to hold you still at night
And back from deep depression
But it's growing and it's growing
This sense that she's been cheat
Because laws and lies all point towards
Women's rights as a two-way street

At 17:
At last, she gallops down the highway
With her hunger and her passion
With eyes that sing for unity
For courage, for compassion
She's sick and tired of waiting
Of being pushed against the shelf
For if you want the world to change:

You must make the change yourself.

Cerys McGrath (16)
Sale Grammar School, Sale

World War II: Remember

As the men fearlessly signed up for war
They had no choice, it was the law
The hugs, the kisses and the, "I'll see you soon"
Is something I remember when staring at the moon
I remember...

The first air raid siren that I ever heard
I was panicking a lot while my mama barely cared
She was used to that because of World War I
She was 25 years old when that first begun
She remembers...

I thought of Papa every day
I wondered if he had already passed away
Just the thought of him on the battlefield made me cry
Oh, I didn't want my papa to die
I remember...

Bang! Bang! Crunch! Smash!
Many buildings fell down with an almighty crash
People were dying left and right
The sky seemed even darker on this unforgettable night
We remember...

The war died down six years later, the year 1945
I wished and prayed with all my might that Papa may still be alive

A man came with news about Papa
He was coming back soon, I celebrated with Mama
We remember...

Divine-Gift Afuwape (11)
Sale Grammar School, Sale

The Tree At The Edge Of The Meadow

At the edge of the meadow
Stands me, Apple Tree
I live all alone
But I'm wild and I'm free

First is beautiful autumn
Fiery and strong
With bronze hair, gold gown
And a soft gentle song

My green summer shirt is now
That same golden gown
The folds gently fluttering
Gradually, gently down

Here comes cruel Lady Winter
With her cold icy glare
Leaves my face frozen
And my branches so bare

I cower, getting bullied
In the cold and rain
By winter's friend, Gale
By myself, I feel pain

Oh thank goodness, at long last
Spring dances along
Flowers all over
She sings a sweet bird song

My branches bloom and blossom
I am pink and white
Tiny leaves emerge
And life is cheery and bright

Summer prances in proudly
Shirt flies in the breeze
Gold hair like the sun
I melt; in winter: freeze

Regard my great green shirt now
As I spread my seeds
My apples are loved
Found in animal feeds

And now I push through once more
The cold and the rain
The hot and the sun
As it all starts again.

Amelie Watson (11)
Sale Grammar School, Sale

The Leviathan

A dragon huge in size slumbered in the waves
Its stomach burned orange with magma
Seeking to make humanity slaves
First it must fight the crab, Tagma

The creature's mouth turned hot and red
Preparing to spit lava onto the sea titan
But it stabbed the leviathan, and it bled
Through anger, its mouth began to brighten

It blasted liquid rock at its rival
Bit and clawed at its arthropod nemesis
The creature perished and failed survival
To dispose of the body, it prepared for emesis

But then another creature ambushed it
A cephalopod beast constricted the dragon
And dropped the leviathan into a pit
It thought it was the legendary Kraken

Then the leviathan sonically roared
Crippling the Kraken, killing it instantly
The leviathan would fight for its hoard
The Kraken began to rot, minutely

The leviathan, a monster of the seas
It swam to the surface in triumph
Then harmed the city with ease
And it had won

Samuel Segree (11)
Sale Grammar School, Sale

A Golden Time

The world of autumn has risen
A golden light,
A river of colours in the night,
An autumn so bright.

An oak so lonely
As autumn slowly,
Takes its toll,
It sits like a beach with no shells,
The crisp and misty air encloses over its bark,
Squirrels scuttle among the tree larks,
Kissing the leaves goodbye,
As they float to the stars,
Autumn has begun.

Halloween is finally here,
Candy and treats everywhere,
Golden stars shine bright in the night,
Hiding, what may the gloomy dark hold,
No one knows until they are told,
Of scary monsters with eyes of gold,
The oak, decorated in twinkly lights,
Helping children find their way in the night,
No longer alone,
As its company has grown,
Halloween has finally arrived.

Now, autumn is almost over,
Winter's coming soon,
The winter moon,
Is coming too,
Crunchy leaves fall until they have all fallen,
Snow might be here,
No need to shed a tear,
That autumn's gone, bring winter on.

Amelia Miah-Earl
Sale Grammar School, Sale

Think Again

Summer brings laughter and fun
Picnic joy for everyone
When the precious sun goes down
Litter infests our dark town
People feast on things to eat
Rubbish will be at Earth's feet
So, think again

Autumn brings those falling leaves
From the trees and through the breeze
Deforestation looms ahead
The trees will no longer shed
No more fresh leaves on the ground
Newly built houses all around
So, think again

Winter brings freezing, cold snow
Children playing - then letting go
Global warming is here to stay
The snow will soon fade away
You may think, *yes, no more cold*
Excessive heat will get old
So, think again

Spring brings the new out to play
Lambs and chicks born in the hay

Our animals will be killed
Just so our stomachs are filled
Not all people will get to eat
We're chomping in comfy seats
So, think again.

Jessie Morgan (12)
Sale Grammar School, Sale

Where Is Your Heart ?

Haiku poetry

Soft fingers of cool
Play the grass like a fiddle
A relieving breeze

Never feel alone
Rushes are gently rustling
Whispering voices

Meadows slightly sway
Dancing to unheard music
Everywhere's alive

Will we be alone?
Can you tell us that you're sure
On Earth our own home

Our future you built
On haphazard, wobbly stilts
How long will it last?

Forest fires burning
Death caused by global warming
Did you think it through?

Famine and yearning
Your fault as much as ours
Did you try to help?

Oceans are churning
With melted ice, they're rising
Did you consider?

People are learning
That our time could be too late
We need action now

So we do our part
You tear our future apart
And where is your heart?

Zoe Chaffer (14)
Sale Grammar School, Sale

The Reverse Journey To Acceptance

I walk down the corridor
People want to be like me
Pretty, popular
As lovely as can be

Yet I walk into the bathroom
Remove my fake face
My spots are visible
I'm finally out of my case

My hair in a ponytail
No longer flowing
I add my glasses
And finally, get going

I walk down the corridor
People look me up and down
Disgusted impressions fill their faces
I can't help but frown

I try to feel confident
Showing the world my natural beauty
Look at me, flying solo
No longer a cutie

Feeling confident is no longer possible
Their 'beauty needs' I no longer abide
A smile covers my face
But I feel inside, they've stolen my pride.

Olivia Inglis (11)
Sale Grammar School, Sale

How To Daydream

To have a daydream,
All that you do,
Is let go of thoughts,
And think about you.

You let your mind wander,
Or go for a stroll,
To let you escape,
When life takes its toll.

Then you go to a place,
Only you can go,
Where there are yetis,
And your happiness grows.

Now there is a difference,
Between dreams and daydreams,
That you must register,
Before they blend at the seams.

In dreams you sleep,
And see unrealistic scenes,
In daydreams you think,
And wonder about fantasies.

Now that you know,
What to do,
Just let go of your thoughts,
And think about you.

Clara Hayward (11)
Sale Grammar School, Sale

The Love I Gave

The love I gave
In 100 different ways
The memories we shared
They showed you cared
Everything I used to do
I did all in the thought of you
I would never stop making you smile
Not even for a short while
You meant the world to me
But now it's clear to see
We are nothing but a memory

But I'm staying strong
It's time for me to move on
I loved you - I knew it was wrong
But at least now I have a beautiful song
Now life is good
Because I've put down my hood
Now I see life
In a whole new light
And I'm gonna let
My light shine so bright.

Enoch Oluga (13)
Sale Grammar School, Sale

Don't Just Stand By

Why are we still needing
To leave trash around our cities
Leaving air intoxicating
Doing nothing - 'cause we're still breathing?

What are we doing?
Being too exaggerating
On the problems that we're facing
Yet still no change: it's disgracing.

I don't understand
Why we aren't a helping hand
'Cause if we don't fix and mend
Then this world won't go to plan.

So how about we try
To keep this world's health high?
Help it grow and beautify,
Come on now, don't just stand by!

Florence Munt (13)
Sale Grammar School, Sale

Arctic Foxes' Devastation

Thick, crisp snow
Shards like knives
But little did we know
It was saving our lives

As the ice began to thaw
And our pack began to cry
It was monsters that we saw
And they would not say goodbye

As our forest began to grow smaller
Less and less food for us to eat
All the other creatures were stronger, taller
And in fights, we had to face defeat

Our red southern cousins are taking our lands
We pray for winter to arrive
Our underlying fate is in your hands
Without you, we will not survive...

Evangeline Streeter (11)
Sale Grammar School, Sale

The Journey Of A Glacier

The journey of a glacier
A towering dreadnought of ice
A colossal might of nature
Making gods look like mice

The journey of a glacier
Drifting through a field of snow
The ice, it denatures
Cutting through the floe

The journey of a glacier
A ship on stormy seas
Waves smashing its facia
A prow like Swiss cheese

The journey of a glacier
Laying down to rest
Coming to embrace her
The land, its final nest

The fate of a glacier set in stone
To be one with the land, now its own.

Max Howarth (11)
Sale Grammar School, Sale

War

Fires blaze
Bombs fall
Guns shoot
But what for?

People scream
Houses burn
Innocent die
And we never learn

If you hide
You will be found
Try to float
And you will drown

You leave your home
Families part
All for the desires
In a selfish man's heart

We never learn
We never change
Like trying to flee
From a bolted cage

The point of war?
It doesn't exist
Put it to an end
This cannot persist.

Liliya Grant (11)
Sale Grammar School, Sale

Discrimination

Smack
A hit
Crunch
Another
Discrimination, I hate it.

Why do bullies bother?
Everyone is different so why
Do we care
About someone's interests
Or the colour of their hair?

It's time to stop!
Bullies take a rest.
Stand by the side of those who need it
As when we go to school
No one should hide.

If we stand together,
With everyone else too,
Then maybe, just maybe
We can get this message through.

Amber Schofield (13)
Sale Grammar School, Sale

Sleep Is Undervalued

Sleep is undervalued.
At least by those who matter...
We get up, we work
Work, work, work
And settle down for blissful sleep

But all we get is a few measly hours, before
We get up to
Work, work, work again

Not alert
Not at our best
Not even functioning humans

And those who set our work hours
Don't work our work hours
They can sleep in
And enjoy blissful sleep

Oh, so blissful sleep.

Bilbo Edmondson (14)
Sale Grammar School, Sale

No Ordinary Life

N ormal lives thrive
O rdinary lives dwell

O ptimistically rife
R esurrecting past angry swells
D ying in our mind
I nstantly forgotten
N ow only behind
A s well as begotten
R ifts can form
Y es, left to burn

L ife occurs
I n impromptu hell
F ree energies electrify
E ndless expeditions die.

Rehan Pabby (13)
Sale Grammar School, Sale

Helpless

Clawing, and flailing
Desperately clinging on
My aching limbs are wailing
Why are you gone?

All hope is fleeting
Yet I still believe
My life is succeeding
Why did you leave?

My regret is haunting
Only if I knew
My death is daunting
Why does the punishment come to me
Not you?

You left me here
All alone to die
You thought I'd rot
Hah!
I'm still alive.

Lucy Ashworth (11)
Sale Grammar School, Sale

By A Thread

A singular red string
tying the fates of two
intertwining all that they are
stitched together by their pinkies

my red string is tangled
a knotted mess
unable to find its seamstress
lost in others' embroidery

I'd rather sever it
cut off its bind
than be tethered to the possibilities
the what ifs, could haves

I'd rather fray.

Gabrielle Zhaoying Lin
Sale Grammar School, Sale

A Poem About Flying

A bird
A bee
As I scrape towards the falling stars
Away from the shrinking cars
The sparkling light
Leaves not a shadow
As my trace is covered below
Finally, a time comes
Where so many suns
Fade as I fall
Waiting again to be free.

Will Bond Sykes (13)
Sale Grammar School, Sale

My Little Sister

A knock at the door, she's standing there, an evil grin on her face,
"Get out of my room," I shout loudly, "you're in my personal space!"
I push her out angrily and she lets herself in once more,
My younger sister always makes my insides loudly roar.

If I don't do what she wants or ignore what she states,
She tells on me and there I am washing up all the plates.
Why does she always have to copy everything I do?
She wants to have the exact same white Adidas shoes.

She does not respect my space and thoughts as much as she should,
Well come to think of it, I suppose that this is sisterhood.
She tries to be the same as me and copies what I do,
She wants to have the same room as me painted baby blue.

She will tell my parents lies about me that are not true,
With my own money, for her slime I must buy her some glue.
She moans about her bedtime being earlier than me,
My dad tells her she is younger by three years, three!

After all she is my little sister and so will always be,
She wants to be the same and looks up to me,
The thing she tells me every single week and sometimes more,
Is that being so annoying is what little sisters are for.

Roxanne Jayne Shuttleworth (12)
Sark School, Sark

Choice

Why should a choice
I make when I am twelve
Change how I am treated
When I am old as well
I am a different person now
To the person I will be
It all depends on the choice that makes me me.

Walking along the street
The people I try to speak to
They walk away without a word
They don't like the way I look
They don't like the way I dress
But if I didn't look good
I would feel depressed.

If I eat too much
People accuse me of being fat.
But when I stop eating
I get told to put weight on.
If I put makeup on
I get told to take it off,
But when I don't have any on my face
I get told to put it on as I look like a disgrace

When I ride home on the bus
And I am slumped down in my chair
Then an elderly lady walked up to me
"Young lady you sit up straight in your seat
You will wreck your back and that will be the end."
So I sit up straight and do as she said

Now that I am older
And know what people like
I try to do my best these days
And that I have completed
Everybody likes me
And I do not get judged.

Florence Burletson
Sark School, Sark

The Once Bright Water

The once bright, blue-coloured water
Not a green polluted vessel of plastic after
The rubbish that floats to the surface comes in a bundle
As the ground below comes with a rumble
The wildlife affected comes with a cost
For more and more breeds will be lost
The way it was treated is surely poor
Will rubbish be dumped on the seashore?
And every day and every night
The dead fish will come by
That will sure give you a fright
But for now they will not stop
Destroying wildlife without a hop
So don't get your hopes up, friend
For this surely isn't the end.

Joseph Burn (13)
Sir Robert Pattinson Academy, North Hykeham

Anorexia - A Tale Of An Eating Disorder

One step, two step, there he crept.
As I looked in the mirror and pitifully
Wept. As I studied my body and the
Fact that it's filthily inept. And strange to think of such a
Concept, of one that I am now living in.
Of a child gaining a new asset. One not
Visibly present, but one that lives in their
Mindset. An asset they'd grow to
Resent.

He offered me gifts, great ones in
Fact. And so, me and him formed a promising
Contract as I could not resist. He told me
I'd lose and that sometimes
Less is more. So, I showed him my body, and let him
Preach his score. "Good heavens child, how
Much do you weigh? How often do you buy from the
Store? Nevertheless, I am here to discipline you so that
You shall eat less, day by day."

The twisted. The twisted thoughts
Running around my mind.
Listed. My flaws listed. Now is the time to
Leave them behind.

So some time passes and I have now evolved.
Self-diligence, self-discipline. Just look at how I'm
Beautiful and thin
I sit at the table in front of the cake, in which
Everyone selects a piece, and I feel
Temptation sign its lease. "Surely, I can try a
bit." This contemplation causes him to awake, and decide to
Steal away my youth. "Now is not the time to
Quit. Do not give into your sweet tooth." I shy away
pleading
Guilty and beg the question, "Why can't he ever give me a
Break?"

Some months go by, and I stare, and I stare,
Noticing every change. Sometimes she
Looks smaller, sometimes she looks bigger,
I give a depressive sigh. Sometimes
She looks thinner, sometimes she looks wider
I feel sick. And so I turn the mirror away to
Hide her.
"Put that mirror back where it was, so I can
Check and glare."
I do so and he observes.
Again! He judges me, forcing me to rid of my
Curves.

One less meal, two less meals, anything to keep my
Weight concealed. There are warped images I continue to
see,

And so, I no longer know what's real.
This irritation. This scream inside I feel, only
Seems to grow stronger. I don't know if I can cope much longer. I tell you,

This is what happens when you and the devil make a
Deadly deal. But it'll all be worth it once we reach our
Goal when we have our ideal look. And I shall be ever so
Proud when I tell the world of the toll I took to become the
Perfect girl... right?

The noises up there have finally stopped: I
Look around and I feel good. I have done it,
I have lost the weight, as I bloody should.
But then she comes into the room and the dreaded
Thoughts of his restart to bloom.
He grows. Stronger and stronger. Louder and louder
Shouting. "You should look like her!"
He enjoys it. This misery. This anxiety: he erupts into laughter.
I can't do anything but tear up and stare. I'm his
Best student when it comes to his lessons on how to effectively
Compare. And yet I can never pass the impossible test on who is the
Skinniest.

Some more months meander by, and my
Body feels sore, my body feels weak,

My mind is going numb. Drops may drip from my
Eyes, but blood drips from my thumb. I want people to
Ask me, "What is wrong?" I Imagine just screaming out my
Thoughts. And yet I get especially defensive when they
Beckon and pry.

My life has become one
Hellish dream, one which I cannot awake.
Because he has trapped me in his net, and I don't
Think I will ever escape.

My life is bleak, and here's an example of it - a
Day feels like a week, a week feels like a month, and
A month feels like a year. Mum begs me, "Please eat dear.
Anything you want." I consider her request. I contemplate.
I hold back. Because I know he sits in there, ready to
Taunt, the horrors of me probably. No possibly. "No!"
Probably gaining weight.

My body is lighter, but I feel heavier,
Scraping my feet across the ground. This
Fee that I pay is being credited by the loss of my
Pounds. Every time I lose, he becomes richer; he is very
Greedy indeed - I bet he wears green shoes. And that
Would be very fitting as brain is the soil for this
Deadly growing seed. Its roots believe that I am in need
Of good meddle and toil.

Some weeks wander wispily by and
I don't remember who I am, or rather how to be me.
But that's okay because I look better... right? I mean. At
Least that's what we believe. Of course it's true, even though I do not
Bleed and possibly will never conceive.
But then I juxtapose our thoughts, allowing them to twist and turn.
"Is this better?" I dare ask. But then I crash and burn. He lights me on
Fire, so I jump in the sea of tears, only to drown in my
Fears. I have cried so much that I've created an eighth sea.

But that's okay because he tells me I'm a whale according to the
Number on the scale. The alarm spirals off as I drown
Deeper, and deeper and sink into his arms. And though I want to
Get up, I can't. I feel my heart rate slowing down.
He looks at his work, and gives me a
Wicked smile, while I can do nothing but frown. He carries me through
The dark, all the way through the gloom, and I just
Know this journey I have embarked is not ending anytime
Soon.

And so, I find myself in the hospital room
Where I lie like a lifeless corpse. "I wonder, when I am
Going to die?" I question.

My heart could stop at any given moment,
But he with that knowledge is most content.

This is it. I am losing it. I have gone
Bloody insane. I thought. I
Thought I could do it. I thought I was different.
Someway, somehow, he has managed to penetrate my
Brain. My hands are cold, my eyes itch, my
Stomach is in pain, and my fingers twitch. The
Doctor comes in to talk about my
Weight. "You've lost this much," he says,
And a Joker smile is smeared across my
Face. *What a great day!* I think. All teeth are
Exposed. I take a deep breath of relief, feeling glad I
Accepted the deal that he had proposed.
It doesn't last long because he up there has a go because apparently
I have failed. "That is not nearly enough!"
I try to explain myself, but he still tightens the cuff. He
Tells me I am not yet to be let off the hook, as we have not yet
Covered all the chapters in his black book. He
Constantly calls, to rage and yell, shattering up the phone. His
Tormenting is awful, I cannot cope! I let out a menacing
Groan. He inside slithers within my cage, sending chills that
Creep right down to the bone.

And he never gives shaming a rest. My
Invisible skeletal features are the mark of the
Eating disorder crest. My size it's never enough even
Though I try my very best; I do. I swear! How we
Feel of my appearance is nothing short of the word
Detest. This wretched curse has turned me into something of the
Eternally possessed.

He hovers over me, night and day,
Telling me he is here to stay.
I am within him, I am him. His
Hunger has eaten me away.

Now you see how my mind and I have been
Swallowed up in such a perplexia. Because you
See I am now stuck in the belly, after being
Consumed by the great big beast of
Anorexia.

Lena Christensen (14)
Sir Robert Pattinson Academy, North Hykeham

Miserable War

Bombs thrashing through the woods
Blood dripping down the walls
The blood dripping down the walls reminds me of you
Bombs coming as soon as you shout my name
Being miserable in war makes me want to cry
You don't have enough empathy to come and save me
No one wants to save me
Help me out of this war, I want to demolish this pitiless war
Keep shouting at me, the bombs will demolish this war
You don't have enough strength to pull me down
Keep trying but you won't bring back this war
You will never end me but you will end this war.

Gwendoline Gregory (12)
Sir Robert Pattinson Academy, North Hykeham

The Loved And The Lost

Let us take a tour of 1944
Deep down below, our food packets hollow
Fire in the wind, the struggle is determined
To break us they try, no one will survive
Escape we try but we're stuck in eternity
Oh how well we fight, try as we might
We have still lost our friends at the other end
The boats keep us afloat
To the homes we go
Family and friends gone
The sobbing had only just begun
Mothers and children waiting
For the fathers' lives that had been taken
The crying goes on day and day.

Kayden Merridan (12)
Sir Robert Pattinson Academy, North Hykeham

Differences

I have a disability
and that's okay
because everyone is different
in their own special way.
You can have different-coloured hair
and just not care.
You could have ADHD or epilepsy
or ASD like me
You could be big or small
or short or tall
You could have no legs
or one arm
You could be energetic or calm
Everyone is different in their own special way
Everyone is different and that's okay.

Bethany Kendall (12)
Sir Robert Pattinson Academy, North Hykeham

Pollution

People are treating the world
like it will give them a second chance.
They're slowly destroying the world
without giving it a glance.
Our ice caps melting away
taking animals' habitats with it.
People talk about it but don't take action,
I just don't get it.
Life on Earth is decreasing,
even though some people are giving everything.
Lakes slowly drying up,
now some people can't fill a cup.
Underwater animals feeding on poison
that's been discarded in the sea,
why can't people stop
we shouldn't have to plea.
Trees being cut down for nothing,
we are losing our fresh air,
people know but they are still chopping.
Increased temperature is still harming,
we are losing everything,
isn't that alarming?

Elvie Drinkwater (12)
St David's College, Llandudno

Leaves

Leaves
Leaves
They grow on trees
They blow in the air
And smell like fresh air
As thin as paper
As green as grass
So many won't last
As long as we are here
We will live in fear
Of what will happen
To our future even when in our hands
If we are gone
Nothing will go wrong
As long as it takes
We will never belong
As the world is crumbling
And we still do nothing
It will slowly get worse until there is nothing left
But our selfishness
As it slowly infests.

Elin Lloyd Jones (12)
St David's College, Llandudno

The Shooting Star

I saw a star shoot across the sky,
Blinding the cities as it went by,
Too quick to hold,
Burning so hard it can't get cold,
Good only to make wishes on
And then forever it shall be gone.

Maisie Venables (12)
St David's College, Llandudno

The Future, Our Future

The world is changing,
The world is changing in good and bad ways,
Some people do not agree, but I do,
These are some of the reasons why:

By the year 2050, or even 2025, tens of thousands of animals are gonna be extinct, this is why:
Due to hunting, animal testing, natural disasters and many more causes,
Sea turtles, pandas, koalas, dolphins, sloths and many more are gonna be gone,
Some people may disagree because they kill and carry many diseases,
But in my opinion, they're good because they help the world and keep the forests and jungles alive.

Every year, fifteen billion trees are planted,
But over ten billion of those trees are burned or cut down,
So we are left with only five billion trees each year,
Thousands of people will and do disagree because wood can make tables, chairs and many other things,
But trees produce oxygen and keep us safe.

Chloe McCoy (11)
St Joseph's High School, Crossmaglen

Climate Change

The world is getting destroyed because of climate change.
300 million tons of plastic are made every year.
We shouldn't be littering because animals are getting stuck in plastic bags.
It is really bad for the environment,
And around 5 trillion bits of plastic are found in the ocean.

Animal extinctions are soon going to be a lot.
Sea turtles, pandas, elephants, sloths, dolphins and many more.
Those animals are gonna be extinct around 2050 or even before,
Because of hunting, climate change, animal testing and natural disasters.

Trees burning down; people cut and burn down around 10 billion trees per year!
People argue about this climate change stuff,
People say, "Don't stop littering," and, "Don't stop throwing things in the ocean."
I say, "Do!"
I say that is very disrespectful to our planet!

Karla Garvey (11)
St Joseph's High School, Crossmaglen

Football

Football is the best sport ever
You can't convince me otherwise!
I have tried many other sports
Like GAA, rugby, NBA, NHL, etc.
But football is the best
And it's the most popular sport.

But it's not perfect, there are problems
Like the fans, managers and players' attitudes
I will give you an example: Cristiano Ronaldo
He thinks he's better than everybody
He is very confident,
But he is arguably the best football player of all time.

The football players are very good,
If you look at Ronaldo or Messi,
They both have very good physiques
And are both world class at 37 and 35.
All footballers train very hard.

Raiens Bergers (11)
St Joseph's High School, Crossmaglen

Gaelic Football

Gaelic football is the best sport,
Anybody can play.
Whether you're big, tall, small or short,
Gaelic football is the best sport!

Gaelic football is just so good,
You should try it, you really should.
I'd play forever if I could,
Gaelic football is so good!

Gaelic football is the best,
You can't change my mind.
There's no sport better than it that you will ever find,
Gaelic football is the best!

Gaelic football is the best sport there could be,
I've been playing for so long now and it's never bored me.
But that's not all about this sport,
To join a club, it's completely free!

Cillian Carragher (12)
St Joseph's High School, Crossmaglen

Farming

Farming is the best because
Sheep give you wool
Cows give you milk
Pigs give you pork
Goats give you milk too
What do horses give you? Foals.
Foals? What? Yes, you heard me.
What do tractors give you?
They give you power, they give you power!

The hours you put in to feed them
The hours that you do in a day
You feed the animals day and night
From darkness until the sun comes up bright.

Tractors work hard every day
Tractors pull things like trailers, ploughs and seeders.
Teleporters lift stuff like buckets, pallet forks and
bale spikes.

Fionán McAvoy (11)
St Joseph's High School, Crossmaglen

Save The Bees

Bees are the best bug of the lot
Convince me otherwise, you cannot
They don't attack us like those wasps
But if they do, it comes at a cost
They take pollen to their hive
Where all the bees live and thrive.

But to every good, there is a bad
And usually it is quite, quite sad
So we have to face it, they're becoming extinct
And they could go in just one blink!

So we have to help the bees because they're going to go
And it's because their population is getting low
So do your best to help the bees
And do your part will you, please?

Liam McShane (11)
St Joseph's High School, Crossmaglen

Gaelic Is Better Than Soccer

Gaelic is better than soccer,
You can't even argue.
Everything about Gaelic is good,
And I'll say it again,
Gaelic is better than soccer!

You might think: *Gaelic, better? No!*
Soccer is a world sport, so it's better.
I never thought that,
I always knew Gaelic was better.
70,000 people went to the Champions League Final,
But 85,000 went to the All-Ireland Final.

The passion of the fans,
The scenes when they score,
The points and goals scored,
That's why Gaelic is better!

Pearse Donnelly (12)
St Joseph's High School, Crossmaglen

Bullying Is Wrong!

Breaktime, "Oh no!"
I wonder what the bullies will do today.
Pull my tie, call me names,
Laugh at me, or something else?

This made me hate school so much,
I was sad, scared, upset.
Mum asked me, "What is wrong?"
Should I tell her? Would you tell her?

I told Mum, she didn't take it lightly,
We drove to the school
We went straight to the principal's office.
Fast forward half an hour,
My problem was sorted!

So be strong, take a stand,
Be brave, stop bullying!

Jack McMahon (12)
St Joseph's High School, Crossmaglen

Chicken Nuggets

Chicken nuggets are the best,
You won't convince me otherwise!
Plenty and plenty of chicken I've tried,
And let me tell you,
Chicken nuggets are the best!

You might think:
A chicken in a nugget? Urgh, no thanks!
I always used to think that too!
But then I tried it out,
And oh my! What a revelation!
And what a cause of celebration!

The burst of crumbs
I advise you to try it out.
They're actually really nice,
Chicken nuggets are the best!

Daithi Farrell (11)
St Joseph's High School, Crossmaglen

There Is Nothing Better Than Football

Football is the best sport,
You can't tell me otherwise.
I've played so many sports
And football is just the best!

You might think: *football, no way!*
But I think otherwise for a number of reasons.
Firstly, anyone can play it.
Secondly, it is played worldwide,
So you can play it anywhere!

The thrill and excitement
Of scoring a goal is incomparable!
It's also great exercise
And you can make new friends.
Football is the best sport!

Darragh Murphy (11)
St Joseph's High School, Crossmaglen

End All Bullying!

It's not right to tease other people,
Think of how they feel,
You wouldn't like it,
Now, if you don't mind,
Can you stop it?

What is helpful about being a bully?
All the people surrounding you
Are not even your friends,
So why are you doing this?
Just to feel good?

Why are you doing this to other people?
They could be going through things at home,
And we wouldn't even know.
So do you get where I'm coming from?

Carley Crosby (11)
St Joseph's High School, Crossmaglen

Littering Is Bad

Put rubbish in the bin,
Just throw it in.
Just lift your arm,
The world will be harmed.

Don't be lazy,
You'll be sorry.
If you don't,
You might harm the world.

"One bit of plastic,
Won't make the world worse."
It will, I'm sure.
"One bit of rubbish in the bin,
Won't make the world any better."
The world has already been harmed.
If there's a bin beside you,
Use it!

Abbie Marron (11)
St Joseph's High School, Crossmaglen

Taekwondo

Taekwondo is a competitive sport
Especially when it comes to competitions
Bloodstains all over your dobok
What a feeling when your arm gets raised
So good when you're getting praised!

Once you step onto the mat
Get ready, you're about to get flattened
By me, Tommy the killer!

As soon as the ref's whistle blows
I come in with the first punch. *Pow!*
Blood all over their face
It's a big disgrace!

Thomas Mackin (12)
St Joseph's High School, Crossmaglen

The Best Sport Is Football

The best game is football,
You couldn't tell me any different!
In my eyes, football is the best.
You meet new friends along the way,
And they may even be your best friend.

Football is good for your brain,
It can also lead to a lot of fame.
Some people don't care about fame,
Because they think it's actually quite lame.

The best thing of all,
It makes me really happy,
And I hope it makes you happy too!

Lara Grant (11)
St Joseph's High School, Crossmaglen

Climate Change Has To Come To An End!

Climate change must come to a stop,
If it doesn't, it will be like a big drop!
And the world will have a hole,
Like an old top!

You might think,
That's not my job, it's the government's,
You're a part of the world too!
We must stand together!

The plastic in the ocean,
The sea animals dying,
This needs to come to a stop,
Climate change must come to a stop!

James Duffy (12)
St Joseph's High School, Crossmaglen

Be Who You Are

Most of the time people are discriminated against by society because of their opinions,
What they look like and how they do things.
So many people in the world wish they were different people than they are. Some people want to look different because they think of themselves as ugly or attractive to society,
Because they don't have perfect skin like the people they look at on the Internet.
It is always 100 times better to just be who you are
And your opinion will always be the best for you no matter what anybody thinks.
Being who you are is the best version of yourself that you will ever be.
Celebrate your culture or religion and never be ashamed to be who you truly are.
Being who you are and being happy with yourself will help light shine down on you.
Don't listen to people who discriminate against you for being who you are and not who you want to be.
If you do not feel like you belong or you do not feel like yourself you should do things you enjoy and do it with the people you love and trust.
Never pretend to be somebody you're not.
Be yourself.

Rosie Downie
Tanfield School, Stanley

Pollution Problems

Let's rewind to about 1700
To the start of the Industrial Revolution.
The beginning of England as we know it today.
Medicines, machines, factories.
What could possibly go wrong?
More job opportunities for the poor,
Medicines, cures, vaccines.
All good, right?
But what is that in the air?
A thick, poisonous, toxic gas.
Pollution.
Although the Industrial Revolution brought lots of good,
It brought pollution which was worse than ever before,
Smog clogged the sky and our airways.
Now fast forward to today.
Climate change and global warming at its peak.
Gas in the atmosphere, plastic in the water,
What on Earth have we done?
Careless, thoughtless, clueless about what we are doing to this planet and how fast we are killing our home.
Think, be smart, be aware.
Goodbye pollution.

Kieran O'Neill (13)
Tanfield School, Stanley

It's Time To Change!

People are living on the streets,
It's a disgrace!
They have nothing to eat,
They haven't got their own place.

Are you struggling with bills?
Well, they haven't had anything during this crisis.
They live on the hills,
The city streets, nothing to eat!

So let's change, open up food banks, never mind your bank,
These people don't even have banks!
And you say, get a job?
Well, you need a home to open a bank to get a job!

We must help! And the government?
Well, they don't care about them,
As long as the rich get richer,
Please, just take a moment, to listen.

Please don't judge,
Don't take your anger out, walk in their shoes!
Take a plunge,
Into the world of kindness.

Even if you donate, just a penny,
Pennies add up to pounds! And pounds equal food!
So every penny helps or as they say,
Every little helps!

Noah McNeill (12)
Tanfield School, Stanley

Motivation Is Everything

Motivation is everything.
Every day I believe you can get out of bed in the morning.
I will be proud of you just for that.
Someone has let you down lately?
Don't listen, push through.
Don't give up.
You weren't made just to give up instantly,
You were made because you were special enough too.
Someone in this whole entire world will be believing in you.
If you don't think there is then this poem is for you.
I am proud of you,
You have got out of bed,
At least done something you like and tried something new.
Motivation is everything.
Do not give up, even if someone lets you down.
Just act like it didn't happen.
That's in the past,
The past has already happened but the future hasn't.
Remember, motivation is everything.

Sophia Eilles (11)
Tanfield School, Stanley

Find Out What You Like

F ind out what you like.
I n any case, if someone says you can't do it, believe in yourself.
N ever give up on other people's words.
D on't ever give up on yourself.

Y ou can do it if you keep on trying.
O ne day it will pay off.
U nderstand what you want to do.
R eally believe deep down no matter what people say.

T here might be something bad that happens but keep it going.
R eally, keep going.
U nderestimated, keep it going.
E veryone has hope, even you.

S ee what could happen in the future when it pays off.
E veryone has faith in you.
L ife will be good when it pays off.
F or advice, never give up and just believe in yourself.

Steven Marshall (11)
Tanfield School, Stanley

Save The Animals

Imagine the extinct animals back on Earth,
Seeing megalodons every time you go out to surf.
Dodo birds waddling along the beach,
Waddling towards you, trying to eat your peach.
Dinosaurs roaring through the trees,
Can you feel the buzz like touching a bumblebee?
Can you hear and see?
Woolly mammoths stomping down to forage,
Hearing supersonic booms whilst you are eating your porridge.
Sabertooth tigers climbing up cliffs,
Whilst you are playing your guitar riffs.
Pterodactyls flying through the sky,
Ripping open eagles while you are eating your grandma's apple pie.
But unfortunately, this is never going to happen,
Because of man's polluting the seas, almost killing the Kraken.

Cole Jagger
Tanfield School, Stanley

The Struggles Of Social Anxiety

As the younger generation
we find it hard to come to terms with ourselves.

We have mental health issues getting ignored
and one of the biggest problems is social anxiety.

Have you ever heard, "Stop being so shy,"
or, "Just grow up," from parents?
Have you ever heard, "I have that too?"
from the popular girls that clearly don't.

The real side of social anxiety is having the crushing fear
of talking to people with the overwhelming fear
of being stared at or the centre of attention
and having the mental breakdowns
ones no one can see so it's like wearing a mask
until people aren't around.

Sophie Robinson (12)
Tanfield School, Stanley

A Farewell To Mother Nature

How many times have you admired the trees,
Or the honeybees?
How many times have you gazed at the sea,
Or autumn-time leaves?
How many times have you taken this for granted,
Ignored every flower ever planted?
Mother Nature is dying!
Animals are crying.
Crying out for help but no one seems to care.
No one seems to care about endangered polar bears.
Please next time you see litter on the ground,
Just pick it up, no need for a fuss or a sound.
We need to stand strong and cause a commotion.
To stop people from polluting the ocean.
If we don't come together,
If we don't act fast,
This will be a farewell to Mother Nature at last.

Eve Sidaway (11)
Tanfield School, Stanley

Now Or Never

Why haven't we acted yet?
The effects can be life-changing.
We are aware - but we don't act
It's our planet - our problem.

Deforestation is occurring at a rapid rate
And trees breathe our waste product.
The lungs of our planet - destroyed
It's our planet - our problem.

Deforestation is increasing by the minute
It cools our planet down.
The sun's rays reflect off its surface,
It's our planet - our problem.

We need to act now - before it's too late.
We can't ignore it anymore.
The time to act is now.
It's our planet - our problem.

Dexter Fenwick (13)
Tanfield School, Stanley

Why Be The Same?

H ow and why would you want to be the same when you could be yourself?
O h, when will you learn you will only be yourself, not him or her?
P eople will not like you if you copy them so just be yourself.
E ventually people will like you if you are yourself.

D ream big even if that means jumping 50km!
R each out for your dreams
E ven if you have to fight them!
A nd eventually you will be the best version of you.
M aybe your friends will thank you for helping them.
S o I think by now you should know being yourself is the best thing to do!

Charlie Armstrong (13)
Tanfield School, Stanley

Be Free

You are you, not me,
Beliefs control you, be alive and be free,
Don't let anyone tell you differently.

We are enslaved by the pigs, owned by the wolves
And bought by the rich.
But there is no harm in changing that.

Our dignity will be seen,
You are you, not me.

You will never know if you can do it,
If you don't believe that you can do it.

There's always hope for you to be that person,
That will change the ways of this corrupted world.

Let your destiny be free and cut those chains,
That are holding you back,
Let your name be heard.

Kody Nicholson (12)
Tanfield School, Stanley

How Do You Feel?

How long has it been since you asked yourself, what do I feel?
Instead of saying what everyone wants you to say about yourself.
No matter if you're a geek or nerd you are you,
Others can't change that.
Blond-haired girls may believe they need blue eyes.
Brown-haired girls don't get enough compliments.
Ginger-haired girls mostly get hate.
But we are all beautiful in our own way.
From ballet dancers to stay-at-home moms,
We're all beautiful (so don't be stupid),
Everyone should be treated fairly.
So my question is, do you feel your best?

Annabelle Ferry (12)
Tanfield School, Stanley

Growth

Are you the person to sit down all day?
Are you the person to comfort eat?
Get up, not down,
Work, work, work, work.
Do you have dreams?
Chase them! Don't let the opportunity pass!
Capture it.
Don't allow yourself to fall apart.
Don't crumble like a wall.
You are a force of nature!
Use it!
Don't let haters put you away and lock your hopes.
Don't aspire low,
Set your benchmark higher!
Do better, be better!
Improve yourself!
Build a strong leg, a foundation, a growth mindset!

Marcus Stephenson (13)
Tanfield School, Stanley

World Hunger

W hat has this world come to?
O ranges and apples rotten and full of goo,
R elegations striking again,
L ay for the mourning to function and not only for men,
D oubts for starvation surrender for never.

H ungry children begging for mercy,
U nder the blunder, others eat a pig called Percy,
N ervous souls fighting for life, for
G erms spreading and then children want a scythe,
E erie nights upon no glory,
R ed blood and not a funny story.

Adam Wilkie (11)
Tanfield School, Stanley

Be Yourself

Being yourself isn't a choice,
It's a lifestyle,
You don't need to change yourself to fit in,
Others may not like you, but so what?
Be yourself.

Yourself is perfect,
Being yourself is most important,
You have to be you,
Because being yourself
is being the best of you,
Be yourself.

Being yourself is the most important thing,
Why?
Because then you know who likes you for you,
Then you know who is true
And who will be in your life the most,
Be yourself.

Jess Bartell (12)
Tanfield School, Stanley

Bounce Back Again

B elieve in yourself
O ur lives begin to end the day
U ntil you start believing in yourself even the easy seems impossible
N ew beginnings are often disguised as painful endings
C hange is leading to a new beginning
E very day is a new beginning

B elieve you can and you're halfway there
A journey of a thousand miles begins with a single step
C onfidence equals contentment
K eep going, the expert in everything was once a beginner.

Lacey Tupper (11)
Tanfield School, Stanley

Why Give Up?

Why would you give up?
All because of one mean comment or one small lie?
Life is no time to give up.
Ancestors did not fight for you to lose hope in yourself.
Why give up?
Giving up is a problem for you.
If you give up you give in to lies and comments.
If you give in people will see you as weak
So don't give up on yourself.
Your ancestors. Your family.
Convince others you do not give in or give up
By staying strong. Mentally.
So I ask once again,
Why would you give up?

Rendell Dodd (13)
Tanfield School, Stanley

Why?

Why do people bully gay people or transgenders?
It is really their decision, not ours,
Just because they like their own sex doesn't mean you have to laugh.
You should be supportive
even if you think it's not right,
just keep it to yourself.
If you are one of these bullies I would stop
because if you were gay or lesbian
would you like to be bullied?
I only say this because my uncle is gay
and my grandma is a lesbian
and they get bullied
and this hurts my heart.

Paul Smithson (11)
Tanfield School, Stanley

Stereotypes

S truggles are getting worse,
T erms used against us to make us feel bad,
E ating alone at school,
R ights are getting taken away,
E very day is the same,
O nline bullying is getting worse,
T eachers not caring about it anymore,
Y ounger people growing up too fast,
P hrases are getting used more often against us,
E ntering my mind all the time,
S itting by myself, when will this end? These words hurt us.

Amelia Brandling (11)
Tanfield School, Stanley

Rise Above

Look upon yourself. What do you see?
Success is not a gift.
Success is not easy.
There will be obstacles.
There will be setbacks.
But there are no boundaries.
Life is full of opportunities.

Rise above.
Do what you love.
Don't look back.
You'll fall into the trap!
The way to succeed,
Is to follow the path and proceed.

It will be hard,
It will be challenging,
But I'm sure,
You must endure.

Jamie Scott-Lisle (12)
Tanfield School, Stanley

Save The Animals

Stop!
Is there any way we can stop animal abuse?
It needs to stop.
Lots of animals are being hurt and dying.
Would you like to be hurt? No you wouldn't.
That's why it needs to stop.

There are so many ways it can be stopped.
Donate to the wildlife centre,
Feed animals that are starving,
Don't destroy habitats,
Help endangered animals,
It can all be done.

Animals need a good life too.
Save the animals.

Hannah Brown (11)
Tanfield School, Stanley

Global Warming

G o outside
L ook around
O utside world is beautiful
B eaches, oceans everywhere rubbish lies
A nimals suffering due to our actions
L ittle being done

W orld falling apart
A nyone going to make a change?
R idiculous how people aren't doing anything
M an's doing nothing
I s humanity falling apart
N ot many helping
G o make a change.

Ben Lewins (13)
Tanfield School, Stanley

World Extinction

If we continue this the world could die,
Trees getting cut down leaving us without oxygen,
Rubbish getting thrown into the oceans killing our beloved animals,
Our loving animals being killed and slaughtered for our health,
This is how we treat our world.

As our world slowly fades away in the distance,
The glow of our world exploding,
Our faces and smiles dropping,
The world will die eventually.

Leah Whitney (12)
Tanfield School, Stanley

From Me To You

Pain is temporary
Not forever
But love is legendary
And it is forgiven.

Nobody knows the pain you're in
Only you
So put it to the ground
Never to be found.

Enjoy your journey
It's not forever
Even if it's draining
It will be the best ever.

Live your dreams
Face your fears
Even if it's tears
It's from me to you.

Neve Elliott (12)
Tanfield School, Stanley

Ukrainian War

A lovely city, yes it is like a beam of light,
but then, no food, no supplies.
Nothing at all,
cries for help,
but does anyone respond?

Babies gone,
no family.
Once a lovely city,
now in ruins.
No more homes,
no more city.
Destroyed and gone.

No more people,
no more animals,
no more life.
Just the sound of bombs
and guns.

Jodie Nicolle (11)
Tanfield School, Stanley

You Believe In You

Everyone around you might not believe,
Don't stop believing,
Don't put yourself down,
You can get through this,
You will get through this,
Just keep fighting,
Don't listen to them, they only want to see you fail,
You are everything and more than you think you are,
If you stop now you will prove them right,
Don't stop now,
Even if you feel worthless.

Kara Storey (11)
Tanfield School, Stanley

Autism

A utism awareness. What is it? Why are people named called and judged?
U nique. We are all unique. Autism or not. It's a superpower.
T ime and time again we are treated differently. Why?
I have autism. The bullying is crucial. Why?
S top. We are all equal. It's normal. More than normal.
M aybe think. Autism, is a superpower. Not a disadvantage.

Rhianna Hutchinson (14)
Tanfield School, Stanley

Believe

B elieve in yourself and never ever give up.
E ven if things get hard, always keep trying.
L isten to others, they can teach you things you never
knew before.
I believe we can do anything we put our minds to.
E very day is a new challenge.
V ery important to keep your head up.
E ven though you think you can't do it, guess what, you
can!

Blake Brown (11)
Tanfield School, Stanley

Believe

B e strong and stay strong,
E ven if it feels really long, you should never give up.
L ife is like the weather,
I t can be sunny or rainy where you are.
E very day will get better and closer to your goals,
V ery soon it will get better and better.
E ven if you can reach your goals,

Some day, you will need to believe first!

Riley Graham (11)
Tanfield School, Stanley

Who Are You?

People who judge you, know nothing about you.
Don't pay attention to -
Look at their hair!
What is that outfit?
You are your own style.
You just have to be
The person in the mirror.
Be you.
It's not what's on the outside it's what's on the inside.
There is nothing wrong, with being you.
So let me ask you one question.
Who are you?

Lucy Robson (13)
Tanfield School, Stanley

This Is You

Are you kind to people who are not kind to you?
Do you let other people change who you are?
If you have determination, a positive attitude and kindness
you can do anything.
Nothing is impossible.
It doesn't matter what anyone tells you,
You are yourself and nobody can change that.
If everybody was the same the world would be boring.
Be yourself.

Izzy Norris (11)
Tanfield School, Stanley

Our Responsibility

It's our responsibility to change history,
We learn about history to stop it from repeating
But yet people's voices can't be heard.
People should be accepted for who they are,
What they believe in,
Not to be scared to go down a path by themselves with no support
As everyone should have support to feel believed in.

Lucy Grey (12)
Tanfield School, Stanley

Save Our World

I hope you understand how much this means to me
Protect our world
Just let it be
No need to kill the animals
No need to cut the trees
Because you need to understand
We need it
We need it
Protect our world, save it, please
Because later on you will understand
We need it
We need it.

Isobel Couch (13)
Tanfield School, Stanley

Determination

Why let people bring you down?
Why stop when things get tough?
To be successful you have to sacrifice.
To get your dream you have to give 100 percent.
Don't let them tell you what you can and can't do.
When you think something's too hard, try even harder.
Whatever you do, never give in.

Lloyd Palmer (11)
Tanfield School, Stanley

The Earth's Struggle

Trees getting chopped and chopped,
slowly disappearing.
Buildings here, buildings there,
buildings everywhere.

Golden orbs of fire spreading around the world,
burning to a crisp.
Animals struggling, barely surviving,
trying their best to find food.

Will Taylor (13)
Tanfield School, Stanley

Animal Abuse

A mbushed
N eed to be set free
I n harm
M elancholy
A lone
L ifeless

A nnoyed
B eing starved
U sed for make-up brands and experiments
S tarving
E ndangered.

Rebecca Foreman (11)
Tanfield School, Stanley

My Differences

I may not support their team
but it is just my theme.
I'm not like others.
I'm not a Magpie
but I am Sunderland till I die.
They all hate us
but they are making a silly fuss.
They get angry at us whenever.
I remain Sunderland forever.

Archie Martin (12)
Tanfield School, Stanley

Whirlwind

T hink about what you are doing to our world
O verlooking is bad
R emember it's our world
N o littering
A world like this is special
D on't harm our wonderful world
O ur world is important.

Harry Pound (12)
Tanfield School, Stanley

End War

E verything can be resolved
N ever resolve problems with death
D on't end our problems by killing

W e should talk
A nd never kill anyone
R esolve your problems by talking.

Luke Dover (13)
Tanfield School, Stanley

Success

S peak up
U nderstand your dreams
C hoose positivity and kindness
C hase your dreams
E njoy the journey
S tay stoical
S tay calm.

Lucy Meadows (12)
Tanfield School, Stanley

Our World

Our world is a place of beauty, and our world... was full of space.
Our world is a place of wonder, and our world... was full of grace.
But upon it we build factories, and fill it with waste,
and on it we build houses to home the human race.

We should all know better, and show our great respect,
rather than treating it with misuse and neglect.
But when we're cosy sat at night with heating and light,
does anybody really think of the world and its troubled plight?

Many make their pledges, many make their claims,
but are they for the right reasons? It really is a shame.
We've all begun to see the changes, right before our eyes,
but will we really do enough to unpollute our skies?

Every single person all across the globe,
needs to take their thinking down a different road.
We really need to do our bit, we really need to try,
if the decline of our amazing world - we jointly wish to defy.

Jake Papageorgis (12)
The Beacon School, Banstead

Justice For The Animals!

Around 10% of all plastic is ending up in the sea,
This is not where it is supposed to be,
Fish are getting tangled inside fishing nets,
Within seconds they are strangled, imagine if this was one of your pets.
Sea turtles are growing inside six-pack rings and their shells are becoming deformed,
Within 10 years every animal hospital will be completely swarmed.

46% of all trees have been cut down to make more space,
The animals need to get out! Quick! Pick up the pace!
The animals have nowhere to go now they are all lost,
Wait! There's a poacher ready to kill them for their expensive cost!

In Africa around 100 elephants are killed a day,
White rhinos are already extinct,
Before humans existed tigers were never prey,
But in the last 50 years their population has drastically shrunk.

You think you need to use your car for the five-minute walk to the shop,
A polar bear's home is gone and he is willing for you to stop.
With ice caps melting due to global warming, water levels rise,
A mother sea turtle can't find a place to lay her eggs, no matter how hard she tries.

We are killing animals at an alarming rate,
We must stop now before it's too late!
We need to hurry up, our animal kingdom needs aid,
Let's do something now, before our wildlife continues to fade.

Amelie Smith
The Beacon School, Banstead

Environment Poem

The world is your gift,
Respect it, and let it be.
It's your home not a myth,
So why are you treating it so ungratefully?

I wish there was a way,
A way to make it clear.
The games that we play,
Soon more changes will appear.

First the world is swarming,
Also known as global warming.
Sea levels are now rising,
Yet this is not surprising.

Next there is pollution,
This is no illusion.
It's spread by car exhaust fumes,
That now our air consumes.

Steps staining the earth,
Like blackened coal from the hearth.
Please reduce your carbon footprint,
So listen now and take the hint.

Reduce, reuse, recycle,
Help our Mother Earth.
You could take a ride on your bicycle,
To show how much she's worth.

We need good farming produce,
To provide us with healthy crops.
Food would come in good use,
Because it's not just props.

This all comes under climate change,
Which all sounds rather strange.
This just shows the marks we've left behind,
And the world we've undermined.

These are all my pleas,
All I wish is for consideration.
This is me on two knees,
Begging in desperation.

Phoebe Dobbe (12)
The Beacon School, Banstead

The World Inside My Head

Inside my head there's a world.
A world, I hope, will one day exist.
A world without all the problems we hold,
And without stories left to grow old.

All the problems are coming from us,
Yet we still think it's not a fuss.
Every sky we think is still clear,
Isn't always as it appears.
Driving our cars every day,
Even though it's not going to go away.

But why do we let the trees bleed?
When we keep taking them because of greed.
As our issues continue unravelling,
We still keep on travelling.
Why worry about wealth?
We should be worrying about our planet's health!
Wishing our worries could be solved,
Without our world being dissolved.

Since the air smells of pollution,
There must be a solution.
Pick up your litter,
And don't be a quitter!
The world needs us to change our ways,
Little by little,

Day by day
Cut down on plastic and we will see,
The world inside my head will someday be.

Isabelle Mosley (12)
The Beacon School, Banstead

The Field Of Dandelions

The wind coursed through her hair; she felt so free,
Gentle was the feel of the grass,
Standing in a field of dandelions, alone she'd be,
The sky above clear like glass.

Hues of the sunset spread like fire,
Darkness spreading like a disease,
The serene view was enough to inspire,
One that travels overseas.

A sudden wind coldened this magical day,
Sending a shiver down her spine,
Whisking some dandelions away,
Sadness grabbed her like a vine.

"Oh please dandelions, don't go away,"
The young girl ran down the beaten track,
"Please stay for a sunnier day!"
However much she tried, the dandelions wouldn't come back.

Far above the dandelions did go,
Light on the breeze like a feather,
Against the sun the dandelions did glow,
Standing strong against the changing weather.

Into the infinite horizon the dandelions did fly,
Soaring far and wide across the golden sky.

Katie Bennett (12)
The Beacon School, Banstead

Environment

E ndangered animals need help as we are losing many of them.
N ever litter, litter will make sea animals suffocate.
V ery important issues including deforestation which is ruining animals' habitats.
I ce caps are melting due to pollution creating too much heat.
R ecycling can help protect natural resources,
O ceans are suffering the most because of the plastic waste and more.
N ature is being destroyed like lightning before our eyes.
M ass extinction has been more prevalent over the past few decades.
E arth is overheating rapidly and creating it harder for us to live.
N atural disasters like tsunamis are more common due to global warming.
T emperatures are rising everywhere from global warming causing ice caps to melt.

Daisy Blunden
The Beacon School, Banstead

Everything Moves

Everything is moving,
constantly moving.
The world spins.
The oceans move.
The cars move.
We move.
But what if...
we didn't?
What if nothing moved?
What if it all just stopped?
Nobody ever thinks about that,
but I do.
Because soon enough it will happen.
Whether we like it or not.

You might not see it,
you might not hear it,
but somewhere it's happening...
cars coughing out fumes.
Trees tumbling to feed our greed.
Plastic products polluting our planet.
And habitats harmed.

There is still time.
There is still a glimmer of hope beneath the darkness.
And it's up to us to make a change.

Next time you see litter,
pick it up.
Walk, cycle or even take the bus,
recycle what you can,
reuse what you can,
and maybe plant a tree.
Because little by little things will change.
Then everything can keep moving.

Hazel Ward
The Beacon School, Banstead

Environment

Not enough spent.
Cutting down trees,
It's killing the bees.
It's getting worse,
Because of your hearse
Oil's not the solution,
It's causing the pollution.

Gotta stop littering,
In West Wittering.
It's causing global warming,
The scientists are swarming,
Trying to resolve the issue,
Making biodegradable tissues,
But this isn't enough,
We need to do more stuff.

Wildfires are causing panic,
People are scared like they're on the Titanic.
It was caused by an iceberg,
We're getting help from Greta Thunberg,
Firefighters are helping,
But they can't do everything,
We need you to spend,
Or Earth shall end...

Calum Ratcliffe (12)
The Beacon School, Banstead

The Dog And The Cat

Once upon a time,
There was a man walking his dog,
All of a sudden,
There was a lot of fog,
And then they found a cat
That was in a hat,
The man saw loads of rubbish,
All of them picked it up,
And all had good luck,
It didn't even cost a buck.
They went to the beach
And still rubbish in sea,
Then they got ice cream
But it felt like a dream,
They were running out of time,
Then they found a dime,
They had fun picking up rubbish,
The ones who don't pick up rubbish,
Will get punished.

Megan Lowin (12)
The Beacon School, Banstead

Shark Bite

There once was a man on a boat.
He slipped on his coat
And fell off his boat.

Then he said, "Silly old coat!"
Then the shark bit his boat!
And then he found a goat,
That made him float.

He was very thankful
To him for taking him to a moat.
And then he said, "Thank you goat
For taking me to a moat."

Ashton Kingsley
The Beacon School, Banstead

Endangered Animals

Our animals are in danger!
To them we are strangers -
Even though we cause the danger.

Without these animals we would be devastated
That we could not save them!
We drafted something that helped us
To prevent killing innocent animals that needed our help.
Instead of putting them through hell
Then give them wealth!

Fearne Horton (12)
The Beacon School, Banstead

Poor Plastic

P oor plastic damages our oceans every day
L etting our loved and beautiful oceans go to waste
A thing that now may impact us all
S ometimes it's difficult to stay away from plastic
T he creatures are dying though
I f we work together we can do this
C an you help us?

Ellie Judd (12)
The Beacon School, Banstead

The Deep Blue Sea

The sea can change with a click,
Catch it at the wrong time
You'll want to get away real quick.

With the colourful fish
And the dark blue sea,
It's easily the most magnificent thing.

Most of it is playing hide-and-seek,
Waiting for us to go look,
Go see, take a peek.

Loula Sillery
The Beacon School, Banstead

Save The Fish

Fish are in danger,
Save them as it's a favour,
It's not okay to put them behind glass in an aquarium.
Take them back to the sea
Where they would see their family and live a life long.

Phoebe G (13)
The Beacon School, Banstead

Along The Beach

Along the beach
No grass grows, through seas of litter
And down the mountains of stone.
Along the beach
Its cold, dark, icy air and frizzy hair
Bold, blue sea and icy water, full of cold laughter.
Along the beach
We see frosty sand along the land,
No little children making bubbles in the bath.
Soon they will feel nature's wrath.
Along the beach,
The sun becomes sunset,
The seas become still,
Our sands are forever ill,
And we kill our fish,
Our land goes dry,
One day we will have to say goodbye.

Kandra Nicholas (11)
The King Alfred School An Academy, Highbridge

We Need Change

We need change
Whilst some get good pay
Others work for minimum wage
Electricity and gas prices rise
People begin to exhaust
Children pray for food
The system needs to be paused.

As winter approaches
The days shorten
And money encroaches
Heating our homes becomes a struggle
It seems strange
Winter won't be the same
We need change!

Zoe Byrne (14)
The King Alfred School An Academy, Highbridge

Fight For Your Rights

Up and down,
Black and white,
Smile don't frown,
Stand up and fight,
All creatures tall and small,
Plants that crawl along the floor,
Help us care for them all,
Open your heart, don't shut the door.

Katherine Barlow (13)
The King Alfred School An Academy, Highbridge

Misunderstood

"Deal with it."
"You're just being lazy."
"Just stop thinking."
How?
How can I deal with my mind running and running and running:
100mph
Convinced you are taking your last breaths
The feeling of drowning dominating my lungs.
Am I dying?
I did not choose this.
These statements surrounding anxiety
Do not fill me with anger anymore.
They fill me with dread and disappointment.
The dread that one day you will wake up
And realise
This was not a choice.
Mental health issues can stem from
The overstimulation of our fight or flight response.
The reflexes that saved our ancestors millions of years ago.
It's the adaptation of how our brains are wired to condemn basic tasks as scary and fearful.
To label innocent things as life-threatening and dangerous.
Mental health struggles are sometimes chemical imbalances,
Stripping away our hormones:

Serotonin, dopamine
Because adrenaline is being pumped day and night
This was not a choice.
And it scares me that some people share that viewpoint.
You cannot argue with science, my dear.
I dread the day that you will finally understand
And feel what I feel.
The never-ending nervousness
The constant feeling of eyes stabbing the back of you.
And your hands forever feeling like autumn leaves shaking in the wind
Yes you may claim to understand my brain
But even I can't explain the things that overwhelm
All the other parts of the small muscle that controls me.
The brain's complex
More complex than you will ever know.
It's the bodies equivalent to the Mariana sea trench,
The true depths are unknown.
So no, I'm not being lazy or leave class with no reason
I am being swallowed whole by my own being

But you're right.
Deal with it.

Evi Taylor (13)
Towers School & Sixth Form Centre, Kennington

Empathy

What is empathy?
Why is it necessary?
Empathy is putting yourself in another's shoes,
Not because one must but because one should.
Regardless of the circumstances
Empathy is a pathway to knowledge
A way to unmask another's emotional damage.
But to harbour this skill,
People who are not fit to maintain mental stability
will suffer.
Those people dig their own graves
Shovelling others' emotions behind to wallow in a
void of selfishness.
This antagonistic deed will form a domain in the
executor's mindset,
And shatter the shielded attitude of the emphasiser.
One must not neglect their inner emotions,
Although this conflicts with the main message.
One's wellbeing is still significant
And of utmost importance.
One mustn't stray from the roots of which empathy
has sprouted
Waging from how to balance one's chakra is detrimental to
The positive aura of one's morals.

So, I shall ask you this again...
What is empathy?

Pam Ejemai (13)
Towers School & Sixth Form Centre, Kennington

Flaw

Flaw: An imperfection of an object or oneself.
Have you ever done something wrong?
Well, I can answer that for you -
Yes.
You can't say that I'm wrong.

Everyone must have,
You wouldn't be human if you didn't
Yet some consider it a flaw of ours
So, they hide it away in their pockets.

Being ashamed is another reaction to this unruly defect
And I am ashamed to say I am too.
The feeling of doing something wrong is...
Disheartening.

You try so hard to be perfect,
To be the perfect human being,
From your decision-making to your own body
But nothing seems to fit the perfect image.

It's not just you that does this,
Society, social media, and peers,
They seem to build the foundation of the perfect image
When they aren't perfect themselves
And that is how we consider ourselves the mistake
in this world.

Lucia Parlar Torrado (11)
Towers School & Sixth Form Centre, Kennington

Tornado In The Kitchen

Pans clanging, food flying
Their stove as hot as the sun
Dinner burning, tap running
The Hoover, like thunder has just begun

Recipes ripping, shopping list disappearing
The cupboards were overflowing
Water overboiling, eggs cracking
The washing-up pile was growing

Spray squirting, tea splattering
This was a disaster in the making
Cake curdling, macaroons exploding
This was a bad form of baking

Popcorn popping, microwave spinning
The bins were filling with untameable junk
Mops mopping, glasses smashing
The dishwasher only screaming, *clunk, clunk*

There was a tornado in the kitchen.

Lilia Stone (12)
Towers School & Sixth Form Centre, Kennington

The Street

In the enchanted breeze,
A storm of golden leaves,
Ducks scuttling in the pond,
Pebbles are skipped in the lake,
Fish are gliding gently,
Coats whistle and blow,
Scattering pieces of bread thrown,
Geese swarm in a rush,
People run gracefully,
Leaves form a golden glaze,
Or an amber glisten,
Slowly temperature decreases,
Dogs bark and fetch broken sticks,
Cats explore climbing on every wall,
Woolly hats are worn,
Streetlights sparkle,
When the moonlight seeps through souls,
All there was to hear was an ear-piercing silence,
Games of sports end,
Until the sunlight comes back another day,
Seeds grow in the harsh sunlight,
Willowing trees weep,
Water sparkles in rainfall,
Insects chew on leaves,
Worms wiggle under the earth,

Kites glide with joy,
Campfires ignite with a smoky aura,
Ducks waddle along the surface.

James Milne (12)
Towers School & Sixth Form Centre, Kennington

Trapped

Trapped,
Nowhere to go,
Like a bomb about to explode.
My head spinning,
Still trying to get away.

Anxious,
Now wondering
If I will make it out alive.
My brain was filled
Of strange memories and dreams.

Madness,
Panic filled me.
Unable to escape the fear
I tried to run,
My surroundings stopped me.

Until the day I saw the light.

Tianna Stone (11)
Towers School & Sixth Form Centre, Kennington

Deforestation

Deforestation is like,
Animal extinction
Forests are home to a lot of animals
Do you want to make them extinct?
Please don't cut down our trees
They are wonderful things
They give us oxygen
They help us live
Please save all the animals
I love forests and all the animals in it
So please help me save the animals and the forests
I don't want them to be cut down,
They are so important to us
Trees are amazing so please join me and try to save the trees
Thank you so much for listening, have a safe life.

Ailsa Ballantyne (12)
Uddingston Grammar School, Uddingston

The Day

I walk into my office on a cold winter's day
On the 30th floor I find my way
Into a cubicle with a poster that might say
'Hang in there! You'll be okay!'
I choose not to read it
Because I know that I feed it
The industry Leviathan that no one can slay
And I know I'm not having a bad hair day
The executives arrive with their stylish hair
They pass on despair with every empty stare
I want to scream "Help!" but before I do,
I remember this is all I have.
A soul-crushing workplace with minimal pay
So an empty croak is all I say
The visage breaks, the sickening shroud
I can't escape, it's a malevolent crowd
The CEO is on deck, wearing their cape,
Woven from the pain made by this vast hellscape
It slithers along, speakers in hand
But this time it's not spitting infinite sand.
"They hate each other more than they hate you"
"Don't hold back, market yourself too"
"Become unstoppable no matter what"
"This company relies on you."
It goes back up.

And then I finish the coffee in my cup.
My final despair, the crescendo of pain
From the little money that I gain. I quit my job,
I've outlived my stay
Because this whole company is morally grey.
I go back home.
Then go on to watch a documentary about Rome
I eat some ice cream.
And fall asleep after watching the screen.

Zac Johnston
Uddingston Grammar School, Uddingston

Pollution

We all know pollution is a problem,
Right?
Although we can help it we choose not to.
So if you recycle your rubbish and don't litter,
Our planet will become bigger and bigger
Please put your litter in the bin.

I appreciate your help and all you have done,
I have said my part for today so my time here is done
Until then,
Make sure you pick up your rubbish and put it in the bin,
And all animals will be safe once again.

Kacey Brown
Uddingston Grammar School, Uddingston

My Dog Skyler

My dog Skyler is a rare breed but only in this town,
My dog Skyler likes to eat a lot but has a big heart
to match,
My dog Skyler lies down on my lap after a big meal like
a roast dinner,
My dog Skyler has a beautiful face that not only I love but
everyone else does too,
My dog Skyler gives the best hugs,
My dog Skyler is as funny as a dog can be - she makes
funny faces,
My dog Skyler falls asleep when I stroke her,
My dog Skyler is the best; I love her like no other.

Ashton
Voyage Learning Campus Milton, Worle

Lonely Universe

L ight years away from lurid planets
O nly the dull barren messenger of the Greek gods to keep me company and even they don't stay for long
N o need for a mobile phone, there's no wi-fi in space.
E ven those strange metal creatures that fly around Luna (poor thing, she must be traumatised!) don't see me as someone like them.
L ove is out of bounds for a star, light giver, heat gifter and creator of gods, some say. But an overworked human has a family, so why can't I?
Y ou stand and look at me on a lazy summer's day, but I burn your skin and can blind your eyes - no matter what I do, I'm never favoured.

U nder my lava-like skin, I'm a kind-hearted soul. I love cooking meals, not just skin!
N evertheless, I'm always alone. Not a soul takes trips to see me in a robotic bird.
I 'm coughing and choking all of a sudden. I've never seen space so polluted before.
V ast amounts of smog are being pumped into the air and I realise
E ventually, something of this scale could happen.
R oyal Earth, shades of blue and green. In fact, my favourite planet is a dreary grey colour, with no sign of ice caps or forests, rolling blue oceans or dusty deserts.
S uddenly, I realise. The humans of Earth, I kept them living, their world full of light and made sure they were warm and cosy - and they've ruined it all. Their home is gone.

E arth's civilians lived in poverty and crowdedness, war and pollution, racism and hatred. Yet few of them did anything about it for so long. I had wished to be one of them, but now I know to always be thankful for what I've got. And old Mercury isn't too bad of a neighbour.

Arabella Ingram (12)
Wallace Hall Academy, Thornhill

They'll Think We Are Okay

Cancer, pneumonia, though our knowledge expands,
Countless diseases plague our lands.
But they think we are okay,
Or that things are fine this way.
Our planet, we intoxicate,
And species die at alarming rates.
Still, they think we are okay;
They'll *still* think we are okay.

And as the stars start to align,
They won't take it as a sign.
That we're clearly not okay,
They'll still think we are okay,
And though the ozone will collapse,
And the day could be our last,
They'll think we are okay,
And we've always been okay,
And when creation goes to die,
And they're all up in the sky,
Then they'll know we weren't okay,
And we've never been okay.

Noah James Sheard (13)
Wallace Hall Academy, Thornhill

D-Day

In silence, the children lay,
They had a feeling it was going to be their death day.
The gunshots banged above the bunker,
They knew they weren't going to live any longer.
Their families had already passed away on the battlefields,
As they couldn't keep themselves fully covered.
Now all the children have is their underground bunker,
Knowing if the British fighters didn't win,
They would be talking a different language in the future.
The rivers of blood ran below the soldiers' feet,
While looking at all the dead, wanting to admit defeat.
Thank you to the soldiers that saved our lives,
We now have a day on the 11th of November,
To remember you all saving our lives.

Sophia Williamson (12)
Wallace Hall Academy, Thornhill

In The Dead Of Night

As I stand there in the dead of night,
The birds in my hair are having an almighty fight,
Standing as I do every night,
Until something hit me, perhaps a meteor,
A bottle, a can, or maybe a rubber ball,
Crisp packets, tyres, I've seen it all,
But nothing like this,
Why this could be gentle,
Because they're taking away all,
The bottles, the cans, even the rubber ball,
Crisp packets, tyres, now I have seen it all,
This is a friend that I see,
And they don't see this as a chore,
But a simple necessity,
Oh, it is such a sight to see,
Somebody caring for me,
The birds in my hair have finished their fight,
As I stand there in the dead of night.

Emily Allen (12)
Wallace Hall Academy, Thornhill

Struggles Of The War

On the battlefield,
Lie the dead,
Just because the people in power,
Want their opposition shot in the head.

Depression ever glooms,
Over the ones at home,
Knowing their beloveds,
Might have been killed in the forbidden zone.

Gunfire will be heard,
Every day and every night,
And when blood falls on your hands,
The sadness that you caused,
You will understand.

It is a hard time for all,
Waiting on the powerful to cry the ending call,
So the struggles of the war,
Can vanish once and for all.

Daniel McBride (13)
Wallace Hall Academy, Thornhill

Nettle

N ettle, you're a sly green devil, lurking at roadsides amongst the overgrown verge, for an unsuspecting victim to cross your path.
E very innocent that hops past receives the same treatment. Red-hot spikes prick the casualty, causing stinging irritation, a
T ingling sensation, mass infuriation.
T otal condemnation! Yet you stand tall as white bumps rise.
L aughing in the long grass, between the large bushes, the silent
E nemy lurking by the forest path. But take note, Nettle, one of these days, I'll make you into soup!

L M Owens (12)
Wallace Hall Academy, Thornhill

We All Need To Change

Hearts are pumping
Hearts are stopping
Lives are valuable
But lives to you are nothing
Oceans are homes
Trees are homes
Nature is all of our homes
But lives to you are nothing
What you don't get is
We love our surroundings
We love to have fun
We love our friends and family
But now we can't
You're destroying our homes
You make them unsafe
Our nature is struggling
We are struggling
Have some respect for the people
Who want to live happily
And change now.

Khloe Harkness (12)
Wallace Hall Academy, Thornhill

I Can't Explain

It's like a thumping in my chest,
All I need is a rest.
I walk around like nothing's wrong,
When inside I'm singing a different song.

I shake a lot, it's meant to happen,
Then all of a sudden, I'm really crabbit
I try to stay quiet,
It's what I think I should do.

But now it's hard for a redo,
I laugh and cry.
I'm sometimes bright, I'm sometimes shy.
But I have to keep going until it's goodbye.

Skye Ross (12)
Wallace Hall Academy, Thornhill

The Tree On The Hill

As I sit on the hill, I fee! the wind,
Blowing through my branches and leaves.
I see the whole town staring back at me.

I sit on the hill 365 days a year,
I get a new coat,
Reds, oranges, yellows and sometimes bare.
As time goes on, I get chopped down,
I get thrown into a machine,
To get shredded up and driven away.

I get made into different things,
Paper, cardboard, books,
But always remember,
I was the tree on the hill.

Lucas Minaudo (12)
Wallace Hall Academy, Thornhill

What Can I Do To Be You?

What can I do to be you?
Wishing and dreaming,
What else can I do?

What can I do to be you?
I'm not skinny, I'm not small,
I don't have any... at all.

What can I do to be you?
My hair isn't straight,
My hair isn't long,
It's hard to believe my fate.

What can I do to be you?
I'm not strong,
I'm not rich,
Everything she says feels like a song.

What can I do to be you?

Emilia Forsyth (12)
Wallace Hall Academy, Thornhill

Rights For Everyone

The people in our country have many rights,
But people in other countries might not have any rights.
We need to think about what we have and others don't,
Like the Jews in Germany couldn't even vote.
There are lots of things people can and can't do,
Black people were separated from everyone else,
Schools, hotels, almost every single building,
Everyone should have the same rights,
No matter if you're African, Asian or European.

Oliver Cowan (12)
Wallace Hall Academy, Thornhill

To Be Like Them

To be like Roy Keane,
It would be a dream.
The price I would pay,
Just to play.
Whoever you are,
You can be the next Neymar.
Doesn't matter if you're not as good as de Gea,
You're still a good player.
Doesn't matter about anything,
You don't need to play like Dean...
Just follow your dream!

Seth Ricky McKie (12)
Wallace Hall Academy, Thornhill

Financial Crisis

F inancially
I n a
N ational
A lteration
N o one
C an
I dentify
A ny
L ife balance

C ome
R ound,
I nside
S omeone else
I s
S aviour.

Iona McVey (12)
Wallace Hall Academy, Thornhill

The Turn

Leaves turn orange, red and yellow,
Twirling and swirling through the foggy, thick mist.
Falling
Ever so
Steadily
Like skeletons, the trees were on a fire-lit blanket.
The wind blew the long dead dancing grass and it
Turned...
And it turned...
The turn.

Murrin Halliday (13)
Wallace Hall Academy, Thornhill

The Night Went On

I heard a noise that made me startle,
In the sky, there was a sparkle.
As the night went on,
I sang a song.
In the distance, I heard a growl
Then I heard something howl.

Abbi Gray (13)
Wallace Hall Academy, Thornhill

I Shall Protect The Forests

Have you ever really looked at trees,
And seen their perfect beauty?
If you have, you'll know that their protection
Is a stern and sacred duty.

Protection of that spreading grandeur,
Through many summers grown.
Safeguarding those temples green
Where the song of birds is known.

Then remember that the forest fire
Is an enemy to fight.
It is a tree assassin to be
Watched both day and night.

A campfire left unguarded,
A match tossed carelessly,
May bring destruction with great loss,
And deepest tragedy.

When next you see the wide-flung branches
Of a graceful pine,
Think to yourself, a sacred service
Is part and parcel of mine.

I resolve to protect all trees forever,
And guard their heaven-sent beauty,
To save the forests of our land
Shall ever be my duty.

Sami Magali (11)
Whitefield School, Cricklewood

The Climate Is Changing

The climate is changing
What does that mean?
Some say "Don't worry!
It's not what it seems!"

But it seems to me
Each summer I have lived
Gets hotter and hotter
Stroud is now Madrid

The government declares
"Don't worry! Nothing to fear"
But I don't feel they're listening
And that's hard to bear.

This summer was unbearable
Imagine it heats more
What then?
Okay if you're rich
But maybe not if you're poor.

This heat is caused by us,
Our emissions, not by chance
It's heat that scorches
Burn, dries, kills all plants.

I've seen brown fields, burnt trees
No green anywhere
Parched riverbeds, dead fish...
It fills me with despair.

In the end who gets hurt?
It'll be us, the young
But why should we bear the burden
Seems to me that's wrong.

The climate is changing really
What does that mean??
It's not changing, it's ecocide.
To stay silent...
...is obscene.

Noma McBurney (13)
Wycliffe College, Stonehouse

Just A Few Of The Many Problems Around The World

How happy is hunger starvation?
Does the starvation make you shiver?
Does it?
It changes lives, makes them painful.
Does the starvation make you shiver?
Does it?
Is this a world that you want to live in?

How happy is discrimination?
Why would you think discrimination is right?
The discrimination is the worst social control of all.
Down, down, down into the darkness of discrimination.
Gently it goes - the unethical, the inappropriate, the terrible.
It changes lives and makes them painful!
Is this a world that you want to live in?

How happy is climate change?
Pakistan going underwater.
People having to move from their houses.
Disease spreading everywhere.
Just so we can live our everyday lives.

Is this right? Should we be doing this?
is this a world that we want to be living in?

Jonathan Phillips (13)
Wycliffe College, Stonehouse

A Perfect World

No pollution,
No climate change,
No discrimination,
No poverty.

That's what I dream of,
That's what we all dream of.

No starving adults and children,
No rape or slavery,
No adults who just want more money,
Freedom of speech.

But we can't have it,
Not just yet.
Perfect is not capable for us humans.
We are too envious, greedy, always wanting more.
Thinking more about ourselves than others.

But if we lived in a perfect world,
There would be no mistakes,
No problems,
Nothing we could improve on or fix.

So instead of looking back at the past,
Let's look towards the future,
And build a healthy and sustainable environment
For the generations to come.

And reach as close as we can get
To a perfect world.

Conrad Mosimann (13)
Wycliffe College, Stonehouse

Litter

She's a doctor, she saves lives
For her beautiful family she provides
She's happy and she wants nothing more
But she didn't pick that bottle from the floor

He's a CEO, he's always working
Gifting his loved ones with all he's earning
He's happy and he wants nothing more
But he didn't pick that paper from the floor

Generations are happy that they're still around
But who's going to be the person to look at the ground
Scattered with plastic and nylon and more
So, who's going to be the one to clean up the floor?

They're young and focusing on their education
In order to be the changed generation
They're happy but they want a little bit more
So, they're the ones who pick the litter from the floor.

Aiwansosa Ozakpolor
Wycliffe College, Stonehouse

Change

Change.
Like a clueless caterpillar,
Willing to take the risk,
And the outcome is a beautiful butterfly.

We are all caterpillars,
Having the option to change,
But we never do.
Why?

Like when women were fighting for rights that men were handed,
And men sat back,
Watched,
And made a mockery.
But why would men want to change a world
That suits them so well?

We all think that change is out of our control,
And in the hands of others.
But others think that about us,
So what will you do?

Let others stay cocooned up forever,
Or let them spread their wings and fly.

Emily Gaulton (13)
Wycliffe College, Stonehouse

The Earth

We all have a task from the day of our birth,
and that is to take care of the Earth.

We are ruining our planet and our home,
where greenhouse gases are free to roam.

When we get in the car to go somewhere,
even then we are polluting the air.

In billions of years the time will come,
when the Earth will strike the sun.

Continue like this, there will be no more
creatures, species, habitats galore.

Polar bears are on the hunt for ice,
too warm for them, it's not nice.

This is our home which we must protect,
otherwise, our planet will be wrecked.

Archie Larkman (13)
Wycliffe College, Stonehouse

I Wish For Peace

Tractors capturing invading tanks in the field,
Tractors planting rows of golden sunflowers in the field.

Frightened families sheltering during an air raid in the Metro,
Busy commuters rushing to work in the Metro.

Anti-personnel mines scattered in the playground,
Laughing children swinging high in the playground.

Hungry, frightened dogs defending their bombed-out home,
Calm contented dogs lying in the sunshine outside their home.

I wish for
A world where
Politicians talk
Not fight.

Lily Puxley
Wycliffe College, Stonehouse

Climate Change

Leading to the fight against climate change
Lots of challenges that we will tackle
Global warming is coming soon
But we will still see the sun and moon
What about our planet and trees?
Earth needs some peace
As the planet gets hotter
So does the frozen world
Leading it to melt away along with the wildlife that inhabits it
Climate change is already here
There are lots of things we can't stop
Let us save Mother Nature
Life is pleasant here on Earth
Don't let disaster become her birth.

Jamie Whitbread (13)
Wycliffe College, Stonehouse

Greed

Humanity is the apex species,
control over air, land, and sea,
over plant, bird, bug and tree.

Why then do we destroy our forests,
Why then do we destroy our seas,
Why then do we destroy the plants and animals in
the name of greed?

Why then do we kill each other,
over oil, land and insanity,
Why then do we level cities, incinerate them
all for a little thing called greed?

Tom Cox
Wycliffe College, Stonehouse

Save The Planet

Let's say goodbye to plastic waste
And hello to a safer future
We need to stand up and not be seated
Until we have made an impact
This waste of life causing disruption
Towards turtles, towards our seas and towards everyone
Will cost us
Rise higher than a rubbish wave
And make a meaningful difference.

Imogen Bewsey
Wycliffe College, Stonehouse

Growing Old

Growing old is a natural thing,
Growing old happens to everything,
Growing old means things die,
Growing old is the way of life,
Growing old changes how you look,
Growing old changes your personality,
Growing old makes you slower but you feel time goes quicker.

Kieran Etheridge (13)
Wycliffe College, Stonehouse

The Truth

I often wander to clear my head.
When I see humanity's faults at night.
I rid myself of the existential dread
To witness hate sucked of all its light.
You see the beggars, fools and the lost that roam the street
They are perceived as horrible disgraces.
But I see them in my head as clean as a sheet
For they do not follow people's paces.
After all these people we see at night
They, of course, have a human heart.
For love and passion, they have the ability to fight
And they can be morose as compassion falls apart.
I love these people for they have no reason to sleuth
They are lovers of the night ballad.
And only I understand this to be the truth:
Humanity lies with those who bear hearts and that is
always valid.

Jack Roberts (16)
Ysgol Gyfun Cwm Rhymni, Fleur De Lys

YOUNG WRITERS INFORMATION

We hope you have enjoyed reading this book – and that you will continue to in the coming years.

If you're the parent or family member of an enthusiastic poet or story writer, do visit our website **www.youngwriters.co.uk/subscribe** and sign up to receive news, competitions, writing challenges and tips, activities and much, much more! There's lots to keep budding writers motivated!

If you would like to order further copies of this book, or any of our other titles, then please give us a call or order via your online account.

Young Writers
Remus House
Coltsfoot Drive
Peterborough
PE2 9BF
(01733) 890066
info@youngwriters.co.uk

Join in the conversation!
Tips, news, giveaways and much more!

YoungWritersUK YoungWritersCW youngwriterscw